# WeightWatchers®
# Deeply
# Delicious

SIMON &
SCHUSTER

London · New York · Sydney · Toronto

A CBS COMPANY

First published in Great Britain by Simon & Schuster UK Ltd, 2008
A CBS Company

Copyright © 2008 Weight Watchers International, Inc.
First published 2008
Second edition published 2011
Simon & Schuster Illustrated Books, Simon & Schuster UK Ltd,
First Floor, 222 Gray's Inn Road, London WC1X 8HB

Weight Watchers Publications Team: Jane Griffiths, Donna Watts, Nina McKerlie and Lucy Vickers.

Photography by Steve Baxter, Iain Bagwell and Steve Lee.
Design and typesetting by Fiona Andreanelli and Tiger Media Ltd.
Printed and bound in Singapore.

A CIP catalogue for this book is available from the British Library

ISBN 978-1-84983-396-7

**ProPoints**® value logo: You'll find this easy to read **ProPoints** value logo on every recipe throughout the book. The logo represents the number of **ProPoints** values per serving each recipe contains. It is not an indication of the fillingness of a recipe.

Weight Watchers **ProPoints** Weight Loss System is a simple way to lose weight. As part of the Weight Watchers **ProPoints** plan you'll enjoy eating delicious, healthy, filling foods that help to keep you feeling satisfied for longer and in control of your portions.

V This symbol denotes a vegetarian recipe and assumes that, where relevant, free range eggs, vegetarian cheese, vegetarian virtually fat free fromage frais, vegetarian low fat crème fraîche and vegetarian low fat yogurts are used. Virtually fat free fromage frais, low fat crème fraîche and low fat yogurts may contain traces of gelatine so they are not always vegetarian. Please check the labels.

❄ This symbol denotes a dish that can be frozen.

**RECIPE NOTES:**

**Egg size:** Medium, unless otherwise stated.

**All fruits and vegetables:** Medium sized, unless otherwise stated.

**Raw eggs:** Only the freshest eggs should be used. Pregnant women, the elderly and children should avoid recipes with eggs that are not fully cooked or raw.

**Stock:** Stock cubes used in recipes, unless otherwise stated. These should be prepared according to packet instructions.

**Recipe timings:** These are approximate and meant to be guidelines. Please note that the preparation time includes all the steps up to and following the main cooking time(s).

**Low fat spread:** Where a recipe states to use a low fat spread, a light spread with a fat content of no less than 38% should be used.

# Contents

*Deeply Delicious* is a collection of recipes from Weight Watchers, full of healthy options, fresh ingredients and inspiration. With *Deeply Delicious* you'll find plenty of ideas to choose from, whether you're treating yourself to a leisurely weekend breakfast, comforting winter warmer, sweet treat, light lunch or quick and easy supper. There are also mouth-watering vegetarian recipes and variations.

*Deeply Delicious* is the ideal cookbook if you are looking to eat healthily. And with a range of recipes that are certain to suit the whole family, you can enjoy mealtimes without compromising your weight loss. With so many fabulous recipes to try, many are certain to become firm favourites.

Hot peppered chicken salad, page 42

# Fluffy breakfast pancakes

*(2 ProPoints value)*

Makes **10** small pancakes **V**

| **ProPoints** values per recipe | 17 | calories per serving | 155 |

These are like the pancakes that you get in America for breakfast in huge portions with maple syrup and bacon or sausages. This is a scrumptious low **ProPoints** value version.

*Preparation and cooking time 25 minutes*

2 eggs, separated
100 g (3½ oz) plain flour
½ teaspoon salt
2 teaspoons baking powder
2 teaspoons caster sugar
150 ml (5 fl oz) skimmed milk
low fat cooking spray

1 Gently heat a large, non stick frying pan or griddle. Whisk the egg whites until stiff. In a large bowl, sift the flour, salt, baking powder and sugar and mix together.

2 In a jug, beat the egg yolks and milk together. Pour this mixture into the dry ingredients and stir until just mixed but do not beat.

3 With a metal spoon, lightly fold in the egg whites. Spray the pan or griddle with the cooking spray and drop the batter on to it in tablespoonfuls. You should be able to cook three or four at the same time.

4 After 1–2 minutes they should be puffed up and bubbly. Flip them over with a palette knife or fish slice and lightly brown the other side.

5 Keep them warm in a low heated oven on a plate covered with foil or a tea towel until they are all cooked.

# Tropical fruit kebabs

*(1 ProPoints value)*

Serves **4 V**

| **ProPoints** values per recipe | 5 | calories per serving | 143 |

*Preparation time 20 minutes*

4 figs, halved
½ pineapple, cut into segments
8 large strawberries
2 bananas, cut into 2.5 cm (1 inch) lengths
2 peaches, quartered
grated zest and juice of 2 oranges
200 g (7 oz) low fat yogurt in any flavour, to serve

1 Soak eight wooden kebab sticks in water for at least 10 minutes to prevent them from burning.

2 Thread five or six pieces of fruit on to each of the wooden kebab sticks and place the kebabs in a large, shallow dish.

3 Mix the orange zest and juice together and pour over the kebabs. Leave to marinate for 10 minutes before placing under a grill or on a barbecue. Cook until the fruit starts to soften and turn golden at the edges. Serve with a bowl of low fat yogurt for dipping.

# Start the day

# Crispy potato cakes

**4** ProPoints value

Serves **4** ❄

| **ProPoints** values per recipe | 16 | calories per serving | 165 |

This makes an excellent brunch when you want something a little bit different. If you like, dish up each serving (two cakes) with a poached egg on top. This will add 2 **ProPoints** values per serving.
*Preparation and cooking time 25 minutes + 10 minutes cooling*

225 g (8 oz) carrots, peeled
450 g (1 lb) floury potatoes, peeled but left whole
1 egg, beaten
1 tablespoon chopped fresh parsley
low fat cooking spray
150 g (5½ oz) turkey rashers
salt and freshly ground black pepper

**1** Bring a pan of water to the boil and simmer the carrots and potatoes for 5 minutes. Drain and let them cool for about 10 minutes, then grate them coarsely.
**2** Mix the grated carrot and potato with the egg, parsley and seasoning.
**3** Heat a heavy, non stick frying pan until very hot and spray it with a little cooking spray. Place 8 large tablespoons of the mixture in the pan, leaving a little space between each one. Flatten them a little with the back of a spoon. You may need to do all this in two batches.
**4** Cook over a low heat for 5 minutes on each side until the potato cakes are golden and cooked through.
**5** Meanwhile, grill the turkey rashers until crispy. Serve two cakes per person topped with the crispy rashers.

TOP TIP  It's quite important to use a floury potato such as King Edward for this recipe – waxy ones will not give the same results.

# All in one breakfast omelette

7 ProPoints value

Serves **1**

| **ProPoints** values per recipe | **7** | calories per serving | **315** |

This is a delicious and healthy breakfast; it's a great kickstart to the day.

*Preparation and cooking time 30 minutes*

25 g (1 oz) lean back bacon rasher
1 teaspoon sunflower oil
100 g (3½ oz) mushrooms, sliced
1 tomato, sliced
2 eggs
2 tablespoons skimmed milk
salt and freshly ground black pepper

**1** Preheat the grill to a medium heat. Grill the bacon until it is crispy. Cut it into strips.
**2** Heat the sunflower oil in a small, non stick frying pan and add the mushrooms. Cook for 5 minutes, until they are softened and then add the tomato slices. Cook for a further 2 minutes. Remove them from the pan and set aside.
**3** Whisk the eggs with the milk and seasoning and pour this into the pan. Cook for 2–3 minutes until you see the edges of the egg setting. Using a wooden spatula, draw the cooked egg into the centre of the pan, allowing the runny, uncooked egg to run to the edges.
**4** When the egg is nearly set, arrange the cooked mushrooms, tomato and strips of grilled bacon on one side of the omelette. Using a spatula, flip the clear half of the omelette over the filling. Carefully slide it on to a warmed serving plate and eat at once.

**VEGETARIAN OPTION** Make sure you use free-range eggs and use a soya bacon rasher instead. Soya bacon rashers are readily available in supermarkets, but remember to alter the **ProPoints** values accordingly.

# Breakfast salad

6 ProPoints value

Serves **4**

| **ProPoints** values per recipe | **25** | calories per serving | **185** |

This substantial salad is perfect for a lunchtime treat or brunch to stave off those hunger pangs.

*Preparation time 15 minutes l Cooking time 15 minutes*

225 g (8 oz) low fat sausages
150 g (5½ oz) lean back bacon
low fat cooking spray
225 g (8 oz) open cup mushrooms, sliced
225 g (8 oz) cherry tomatoes, halved
1 tablespoon wholegrain mustard
1 tablespoon dark soy sauce
1 teaspoon clear honey
350 g (12 oz) Iceberg lettuce, shredded

**1** Grill the sausages for about 10 minutes until evenly browned and cooked through, and grill the bacon until crispy. Slice the sausages into rings and chop the bacon into small pieces.
**2** Meanwhile, spray a frying pan with the cooking spray and add the mushrooms. Cook them for 5 minutes until they are tender. Add the tomatoes, mustard, soy sauce and honey and cook for a further 2 minutes, stirring occasionally. Add the sausages and bacon and mix everything well.
**3** Divide the Iceberg lettuce between four serving plates and top with the 'breakfast' mix. Serve at once.

**VEGETARIAN OPTION** Omit the bacon and use vegetarian sausages instead. The **ProPoints** values will be 3 per serving.

# The big brunch

**9** ProPoints value

Serves **1**

| **ProPoints** values per recipe | 9 | calories per serving | 385 |

Why not spoil yourself over a leisurely weekend brunch? It will set you up for the day.

*Preparation and cooking time 15 minutes*

1 teaspoon vegetable oil
150 g (5½ oz) canned, cooked potatoes or leftover boiled potatoes, sliced thickly
½ small onion, sliced thinly
75 g (2¾ oz) cooked beetroot, chopped into small pieces
50 g (1¾ oz) thick slice cooked ham, cut into strips
1 egg
1 tablespoon half fat crème fraîche
½ teaspoon horseradish relish

**1** Heat the oil in a small frying pan. Fry the potatoes and onion over a high heat until browned. Stir in the beetroot and ham and gently heat through for 5 minutes.
**2** Bring a small pan of water to the boil and poach the egg until lightly set. Mix together the crème fraîche and horseradish.
**3** Spoon the potato mixture on to a hot plate. Top with the poached egg and drizzle on the dressing. Serve.

**TOP TIP** This makes a tasty supper dish too.

**VARIATIONS** Replace the ham with sliced cooked chicken or turkey breast. Smoked haddock fillet (100 g/3½ oz) is delicious, too. The **ProPoints** values per serving will be 9 with chicken, 9 with turkey and 9 with haddock.

# Chilli corn fritters

**5** ProPoints value

Serves **4**

| **ProPoints** values per recipe | 19 | calories per serving | 170 |

You can prepare these tasty cakes up to 2 days before you want to eat them, then just heat through to serve.

*Preparation and cooking time 15 minutes*

50 g (1¾ oz) dried polenta
200 g (7 oz) canned sweetcorn, drained
1 teaspoon chilli flakes
3 tablespoons chopped fresh coriander
1 tablespoon Thai green curry paste
1 tablespoon fish sauce
1 egg
1 tablespoon sunflower oil

**1** Place the polenta in a mixing bowl and stir in the sweetcorn, chilli flakes, coriander, curry paste, fish sauce and egg. Mix together thoroughly until you have a combined sloppy mixture.
**2** Heat a little oil in a frying pan, then drop spoonfuls of the mixture into the pan. Cook over a medium low heat for 3–4 minutes per side until cooked through and golden.

**VARIATION** You can serve these cakes with a cucumber salad to complement their spiciness. Peel and halve a cucumber lengthways. Scoop out the seeds, dice the flesh and mix with 1 tablespoon of rice wine vinegar and a pinch of caster sugar.

# Smoked haddock kedgeree

Serves **4**

| **ProPoints** values per recipe | 38 | calories per serving | 393 |

A classic recipe using smoked haddock, this kedgeree is tasty and substantial. If you keep some smoked haddock fillets in the freezer, try the kedgeree for an impromptu Sunday brunch or quick supper standby.

*Preparation time 20 minutes l Cooking time 30–35 minutes*

300 g (10½ oz) smoked haddock fillets

2 bay leaves

4 whole peppercorns

300 ml (10 fl oz) skimmed milk

low fat cooking spray

2 onions, chopped

225 g (8 oz) dried basmati rice

a pinch of saffron threads, soaked in 2 tablespoons boiling water for 2 minutes

1 tablespoon garam masala

700 ml (1¼ pints) chicken or vegetable stock

a large bunch of fresh parsley, chopped finely, stalks included

200 g (7 oz) very low fat plain fromage frais

salt and freshly ground black pepper

TO GARNISH

2 eggs, hard boiled and quartered

1 lemon, cut into wedges

**1** Place the haddock fillets skin side up in a large pan with the bay leaves and peppercorns. Pour over the milk and bring to the boil; then turn off and leave to cool.

**2** Meanwhile, heat a large, non stick frying pan or wok and spray with the cooking spray. Fry the onions until golden and softened, adding a little water if necessary to prevent them from sticking.

**3** Add the rice, saffron threads with their soaking water and the garam masala, stirring to mix. Then add the stock and bring to the boil, stirring occasionally. Turn down to a gentle simmer and leave to cook for 15 minutes.

**4** Remove the haddock from the milk and flake with your fingers on to a plate, removing the skin and any bones you find as you go. Strain the milk, add it to the rice and stir in.

**5** After about 15–20 minutes, when the rice is just cooked and most of the liquid absorbed, add the flaked haddock, parsley and fromage frais. Stir to heat through. Check the seasoning and serve garnished with the eggs and lemon wedges.

# Bacon and mushroom risotto

13
ProPoints
value

Serves **2**

| **ProPoints** values per recipe | **26** | calories per serving | **450** |

An easy brunch or supper dish made from rice cooked in stock with mushrooms and crispy bacon.

*Preparation time 20 minutes l Cooking time 25 minutes*

4 x 100 g (3½ oz) lean back bacon rashers

100 g (3½ oz) mushrooms, sliced

juice of a lemon

2 dried porcini mushrooms, soaked in 150 ml (5 fl oz) boiling
   water for 10 minutes

low fat cooking spray

1 onion, chopped finely

175 g (6 oz) dried risotto rice

150 ml (5 fl oz) white wine

300 ml (10 fl oz) hot stock

a small bunch of fresh parsley, chopped

salt and freshly ground black pepper

**1** Preheat the grill to high, grill the bacon until crispy then chop into little pieces. Set to one side. Meanwhile, heat a frying pan and add the sliced mushrooms. Season and stir fry for 5 minutes then add the lemon juice and cook for 1 minute until absorbed. Set aside.

**2** Drain the porcini mushrooms, reserving the soaking liquid. Chop finely and add to the cooked mushrooms.

**3** Heat a saucepan and spray with the cooking spray then fry the onion for 4 minutes, until softened. Add the rice, stir, then pour in the wine and porcini soaking liquid and stir vigorously. Add the hot stock a ladleful at a time, waiting until the previous ladleful has been absorbed before adding more, which should take about 5 minutes. Stir between each addition. It will take around 20 minutes before all the stock is absorbed.

**4** Stir in the cooked mushrooms, bacon and parsley, check the seasoning and then serve.

VARIATION Serve with a few shavings of fresh Parmesan cheese (10 g/¼ oz per person) and add 1 **ProPoints** value per serving.

# Mango and raspberry smoothie

Serves **2 V**

| **ProPoints** values per recipe | 1 | calories per serving | 148 |

If you're struggling to find ways to eat all of your 5 a day fruit and vegetable portions, a home made smoothie is an easy way to boost your intake, and it tastes fabulous too.
*Preparation and cooking time 5 minutes*

4 large ice cubes
150 ml (5 fl oz) skimmed milk
1 ripe mango, peeled, stoned and chopped roughly
1 ripe banana, chopped roughly
100 g (3½ oz) frozen raspberries
juice of ½ a lemon

**1** Place the first five ingredients listed in a liquidiser and whizz until smooth, then add lemon juice to taste.
**2** Divide between two tall glasses, add drinking straws and serve immediately.

5 A DAY Using whole fruits in a smoothie means that you get all the healthy fibre, so it's better for you than fruit juice.

TOP TIP To prepare a mango, start by removing the skin with a vegetable peeler. Mangoes have a large flat stone in the middle, so slice down each side of the stone with a knife to remove most of the flesh, then cut away any mango still attached around the stone.

# Oven-roasted tomato tartlets

Makes **8 V** ❄ *Roasted tomatoes only*

| **ProPoints** values per recipe | 16 | calories per serving | 120 |

Slow roasting tomatoes brings out their wonderful rich flavour.
*Preparation time 15 minutes l Cooking time 1¼ hours*

1 kg (2 lb 4 oz) plum tomatoes
1 teaspoon salt
8 x 15 g filo pastry sheets
2 tablespoons olive oil
2 tablespoons fresh basil leaves, torn (optional)
freshly ground black pepper

**1** Preheat the oven to Gas Mark 2/150°C/fan oven 130°C.
**2** Slice the tomatoes in half horizontally and arrange cut-side up on a cooling rack. Lift the cooling rack over a baking sheet and then sprinkle the salt over the tomatoes.
**3** Roast the tomatoes in the oven for 1 hour, until they are beginning to dry out a little.
**4** After the tomatoes have cooked, increase the oven temperature to Gas Mark 5/190°C/fan oven 170°C. Cut each sheet of filo pastry in half, brush with olive oil and sandwich two halves together. Press into eight individual tartlet tins, scrunching up the edges with your fingers so the pastry fits into the tins. Brush the insides of the tartlet cases with any remaining olive oil and place a crumpled piece of foil into each one. Bake for 15 minutes, until the pastry is crisp and golden.
**5** Carefully remove the pastry cases from the tins, remove the foil and fill with the roasted tomato halves.
**6** Scatter each tartlet with a little torn basil, if using, and a generous grinding of black pepper.

TOP TIP It's better to tear fresh basil rather than chop it, since this prevents it from bruising.

# Rancher's turkey

Serves **2**

| **ProPoints** values per recipe | 22 | calories per serving | 455 |

A tasty, filling supper for all those hungry ranchers out there.

*Preparation and cooking time 15 minutes*

2 x 175 g (6 oz) turkey breast fillets
low fat cooking spray
1 large tomato, chopped finely
2 tablespoons hickory BBQ sauce
2 lean, rindless, smoked streaky bacon rashers
400 g can baked beans
1 tablespoon Worcestershire sauce
salt and freshly ground black pepper

1 Place the turkey fillets between two sheets of cling film then beat with a rolling pin until flattened to an even thickness. Season on both sides. Heat a large frying pan, spray with the cooking spray, add the turkey fillets and fry for 2 minutes on each side.

2 Preheat the grill and line the grill pan with foil. Mix the tomato with the BBQ sauce. Place the turkey fillets on the grill pan and top each with the tomato mixture and then a piece of bacon.

3 Grill for 3 minutes until the bacon is crispy. Meanwhile, heat the baked beans and stir in the Worcestershire sauce. Pile on to serving plates and top with the turkey.

# Gammon and egg with parsley sauce

Serves **4**

| **ProPoints** values per recipe | 35 | calories per serving | 332 |

This dish goes well with crunchy green vegetables and potatoes mashed with skimmed milk.

*Preparation and cooking time 20 minutes*

150 g (5½ oz) low fat fromage frais
75 g (2¾ oz) low fat soft cheese
3 tablespoons chopped fresh parsley
4 gammon steaks
4 eggs
salt and freshly ground black pepper

1 Whisk together the fromage frais and soft cheese. Heat gently in a small pan and stir in the parsley and seasoning.

2 Heat a grill to medium high and cook the gammon steaks for 6–7 minutes on each side.

3 Bring a pan of water to the boil and poach the eggs.

4 Serve each gammon steak with a poached egg on top, with the parsley sauce spooned over.

# Raspberry yogurt muffins

**5** ProPoints value

Makes **12 V** ❄

| **ProPoints** values per recipe | 63 | calories per serving | 190 |

Muffins are a treat that come from the USA, although you might find that they are twice the size on the other side of the Atlantic. We've made these smaller versions to help keep the **ProPoints** values low.

*Preparation time 15 minutes l Cooking time 15–20 minutes*

300 g (10½ oz) plain white flour

2 teaspoons baking powder

½ teaspoon ground cinnamon

150 g (5½ oz) light muscovado sugar

100 g (3½ oz) fresh raspberries

1 egg

150 g (5½ oz) low fat natural yogurt

150 ml (5 fl oz) skimmed milk

3 tablespoons sunflower oil

**1** Preheat the oven to Gas Mark 6/200°C/fan oven 180°C. Line a 12 hole muffin tray with paper muffin cases, or use squares of greaseproof paper pushed into the holes.

**2** Sift the flour, baking powder and cinnamon into a large mixing bowl. Stir in the sugar and raspberries.

**3** Beat the egg, yogurt, milk and oil together, and then stir this into the dry ingredients, taking care not to over mix. Spoon the muffin mixture into the paper cases.

**4** Bake for 15–20 minutes, until the muffins are risen and golden brown. Cool in the tray for a few minutes, and then transfer the muffins to a wire rack to cool completely.

TOP TIP The secret of successful muffins is to avoid beating the mixture too much when you add the wet ingredients to the dry ones. They need to be lightly stirred together until just combined.

VARIATION Use 100 g (3½ oz) of fresh blueberries instead of raspberries. The **ProPoints** values per serving will remain the same.

# Spicy banana muffins

**3 ProPoints value**

Makes **10 V** ❄ *up to 1 month*

| **ProPoints** values per recipe | 39 | calories per serving | 165 |

A great way to start the day.
*Preparation time 15 minutes l Cooking time 20–25 minutes*

50 g (1¾ oz) low fat spread
200 g (7 oz) plain flour
2 teaspoons baking powder
100 g (3½ oz) caster sugar
1 teaspoon ground cinnamon
2 bananas
juice of a lemon
100 ml (3½ fl oz) skimmed milk
1 egg, beaten

**1** Preheat the oven to Gas Mark 6/200°C/fan oven 180°C. Put 10 paper muffin cases into a muffin tin.

**2** Melt the low fat spread and leave to cool slightly.

**3** Sift the dry ingredients into a large bowl.

**4** Mash the bananas with a fork and 1 teaspoon of the lemon juice.

**5** Mix together the remaining lemon juice, milk, egg and melted low fat spread.

**6** Pour the wet ingredients into the dry ones and stir very carefully – do not over mix.

**7** Gently fold in the mashed banana and then divide the mixture between the paper muffin cases.

**8** Cook in the preheated oven for 20–25 minutes until golden. Cool on a rack or eat slightly warm – delicious.

# Curried parsnip soup

U 2 ProPoints value

Serves **4 V** ❄ *recommended for up to 1 month*

| **ProPoints** values per recipe | **10** | calories per serving | **65** |

Nothing beats a home made, warming soup –
perfect to perk you up on a cold winter's day.
*Preparation time 15 minutes l Cooking time 18–20 minutes*

**low fat cooking spray**
**1 onion, chopped**
**400 g (14 oz) parsnips, peeled and chopped**
**1 teaspoon curry powder**
**1 teaspoon ground ginger**
**1 teaspoon ground cumin**
**850 ml (1½ pints) vegetable stock**
**salt and freshly ground black pepper**

**1** Spray a medium, non stick saucepan with the cooking spray
and sauté the onion for 4–5 minutes until beginning to soften.
**2** Add the parsnips and spices and stir well to coat the
vegetables with the spices.
**3** Pour in the stock, season, bring to the boil and then simmer for
18–20 minutes, until the parsnips are tender.
**4** Take off the heat and leave to cool for a couple of minutes.
**5** When slightly cooled, blend the soup with a hand blender or in
a food processor.
**6** Check the seasoning, reheat and serve.

**VARIATION** For a zero **ProPoints** value alternative, try curried
cauliflower soup. Just substitute a medium cauliflower for the
parsnips and follow the method above.

# Chunky tomato soup

U 1 ProPoints value

Serves **4 V** *without the Worcestershire sauce* ❄ *see tip*

| **ProPoints** values per recipe | **4** | calories per serving | **85** |

The delicate, peppery taste of the rocket leaves
make this tomato soup taste fabulous.
*Preparation time 15 minutes l Cooking time 25 minutes*

**low fat cooking spray**
**1 onion, chopped finely**
**2 garlic cloves, crushed**
**400 g can chopped tomatoes**
**300 ml (10 fl oz) tomato juice**
**300 ml (10 fl oz) vegetable stock**
**1 tablespoon Worcestershire sauce**
**100 ml (3½ fl oz) low fat plain fromage frais**
**salt and freshly ground black pepper**

**100 g (3½ oz) rocket leaves, to serve**

**1** Spray a large, non stick saucepan with the cooking spray and
add the onion and garlic. Cook over a low heat, stirring from time
to time, until the onion has softened but not browned, adding a
little water if it sticks. This will take about 10 minutes.
**2** Add the chopped tomatoes, tomato juice, stock and
Worcestershire sauce and bring to the boil. Reduce the heat,
cover and simmer for 15 minutes. Season to taste.
**3** Stir in the fromage frais and then ladle the soup into four
warmed bowls. Alternatively, you can top the soup with a
spoonful of the fromage frais (about ½ a tablespoon per serving).
Scatter over the rocket leaves and serve.

**TOP TIP** This soup freezes well, but do freeze it before you add
the fromage frais. When you are ready to serve, reheat the soup
and then continue from step 3.

# Light lunches

# Greek potato patties (potato kephtedes)

**6** ProPoints value

Serves **4** V

| *ProPoints* values per recipe | **22** | calories per serving | **235** |

These spicy Greek patties are delicious served with a yogurt and cucumber dip.

*Preparation time 30 minutes + cooling l Cooking time 40 minutes*

750 g (1 lb 10 oz) potatoes, peeled and chopped
low fat cooking spray
a bunch of spring onions, sliced finely
1 red chilli, de-seeded and chopped finely
1 tablespoon olive oil
1 egg, beaten
a small bunch of fresh mint, chopped roughly
salt and freshly ground black pepper

**1** Bring a large pan of water to the boil and cook the potatoes for 20 minutes or until tender. Drain, then mash and season.

**2** Spray a large, non stick frying pan with the cooking spray, then sauté the onions and chilli for 2 minutes. Add a tablespoon of water if they stick.

**3** Mix the onions and chilli into the potato together with the olive oil, egg and mint. Season and leave to cool for 20 minutes.

**4** Preheat the grill to medium and shape the potato mixture into eight patties. Place on a foil-lined grill pan.

**5** Grill the patties for 5 minutes on each side or until golden.

# Stuffed cabbage leaves (dolmades)

Serves **4 V** ❋

| **ProPoints** values per recipe | **29** | calories per serving | **260** |

Authentic Greek 'dolmades' are wrapped in vine or fig leaves but this recipe has been adapted to use the more readily available Savoy cabbage leaves. Cabbage leaves also allow for more filling. Serve hot or cold with lemon slices and fresh dill sprigs or mint, or with tzatziki.

*Preparation time 1 hour l Cooking time 1 hour*

**2 tablespoons pine nut kernels**

**16 Savoy cabbage leaves**

**125 g (4½ oz) dried long grain rice**

**1 onion, chopped finely**

**8 dried apricots, chopped finely**

**4 tablespoons chopped fresh parsley**

**4 tablespoons chopped fresh dill**

**4 tablespoons chopped fresh mint**

**zest and juice of a lemon**

**1 tablespoon olive oil**

**425 ml (15 fl oz) boiling water**

**sea salt and freshly ground black pepper**

**1** Put the pine nut kernels in a dry frying pan and toast over a low heat until they are beginning to brown. Keep an eye on them to make sure that they don't burn.

**2** Wash the the cabbage leaves, bring a pan of water to the boil, then blanch the cabbage leaves in batches of five or six for 5 seconds. Take them out with tongs and drain.

**3** Mix all the remaining ingredients. except the water, together in a bowl.

**4** Line the base of a large, lidded saucepan with a couple of cabbage leaves. To fill the other leaves, place 1 or 2 tablespoons of the stuffing at the stalk end of the leaf and roll once. Then fold in the sides and continue to roll. Secure with cocktail sticks and put in the saucepan. When one layer is complete, sprinkle over some seasoning and then start another.

**5** When all the leaves are used up, place a small inverted plate inside the saucepan and over the top of the stuffed leaves to weigh them all down. Carefully add the boiling water to the pan. Cover and simmer for 50 minutes.

# Salmon and avocado jackets

$11$ ProPoints value

## Serves 4

| ProPoints values per recipe | 46 | calories per serving | 290 |

For a quick and tasty filling for jacket potatoes, Mrs Hallin, a Gold Member from Southsea in Hampshire, whizzes together a few ingredients in her blender and the result is a very tasty light lunch or supper dish.

*Preparation time 5 minutes l Cooking time 1 hour*

4 x 225 g (8 oz) baking potatoes
100 g (3½ oz) smoked salmon trimmings
½ avocado
200 g can tuna in brine or water, drained
2 teaspoons balsamic vinegar
25 g (1 oz) Quark
freshly ground black pepper
chopped fresh parsley or coriander, to garnish

**1** Preheat the oven to Gas Mark 6/200°C/fan oven 180°C.
**2** Bake the potatoes for approximately 1 hour, until tender.
**3** A few minutes before the potatoes are ready, put the salmon trimmings, avocado flesh, tuna, vinegar and Quark into a food processor or blender and whizz together for a few seconds until smooth. Season to taste with a little black pepper.
**4** Make a deep cut in the top of the potatoes, push open and fill each with a quarter of the filling. Serve at once, garnished with chopped fresh parsley or coriander.

**TOP TIP** For a chunkier texture, simply mix together all the filling ingredients with a fork.

**VARIATIONS** You can use lemon or lime juice instead of balsamic vinegar, if you prefer. Instead of using the avocado mixture to fill jacket potatoes, serve with 2 medium slices of hot toast per person. The *ProPoints* values per serving will be 7.

# Sweetcorn and crab soup

$5$ ProPoints value

## Serves 4

| ProPoints values per recipe | 18 | calories per serving | 135 |

A delicious soup filled with sweetcorn and crab – great as a starter or even a light lunch.

*Preparation time 5 minutes l Cooking time 10 minutes*

1 egg white
1 teaspoon sesame oil
1.2 litres (2 pints) chicken stock
275 g (9½ oz) canned or frozen sweetcorn
1 tablespoon soy sauce
2 teaspoons chopped fresh root ginger
2 teaspoons cornflour, mixed with 2 teaspoons water
225 g (8 oz) canned crabmeat, drained
4 spring onions, chopped
freshly ground black pepper

**1** Beat the egg white and sesame oil together and leave to one side.
**2** Bring the stock to the boil in a large pan and add the sweetcorn. Simmer for 5 minutes and then add the soy sauce, ginger, pepper and cornflour paste.
**3** Bring back to the boil, lower the heat to a simmer and add the crabmeat.
**4** Slowly pour in the egg white and sesame oil mixture, stirring constantly.
**5** Sprinkle over the spring onions and serve.

**TOP TIP** When buying fresh ginger, always select firm, unshrivelled pieces and peel off the skin before use.

**VARIATION** Chicken and sweetcorn soup can be made in the same way – substitute the same amount of cooked shredded chicken for the crabmeat. The *ProPoints* values per serving will be 5.

# Quick mushroom pizza stack

5 ProPoints value

Serves **1** V

| **ProPoints** values per recipe | **5** | calories per serving | **290** |

Big juicy field mushrooms are ideal for this quick pizza and taste delicious smothered in cheese.
*Preparation and cooking time 10 minutes*

low fat cooking spray
2 large flat mushrooms
½ onion, sliced thinly
1 slice wholemeal bread
1 tablespoon low fat cream cheese
25 g (1 oz) grated mozzarella light
½ teaspoon fresh chives, snipped, to garnish

**1** Spray a non stick frying pan with the cooking spray and, when it is hot, add the mushrooms and onion and cook for 5 minutes until browned. Set aside.
**2** Preheat the grill to medium and toast one side of the bread until golden. Spread the cream cheese over the untoasted side of the bread.
**3** Top with the mushrooms, onion and mozzarella and grill for 1–2 minutes until the cheese is bubbling and the toast browned. Garnish with the snipped chives.

**TOP TIP** Field mushrooms or large flat mushrooms are big and juicy. If you can't get hold of them, use 75 g (2¾ oz) of the closed cup variety.

# Chilli seafood spaghetti

7 ProPoints value

Serves **4**

| **ProPoints** values per recipe | **30** | calories per serving | **305** |

A great pasta dish with a lovely spicy tomato and seafood sauce.
*Preparation time 6 minutes l Cooking time 10 minutes*

200 g (7 oz) dried spaghetti
low fat cooking spray
1 onion, chopped
¼ teaspoon chilli flakes
400 g can chopped tomatoes
300 g (10½ oz) mixed seafood
2 tablespoons chopped fresh parsley
salt and freshly ground black pepper
50 g (1¾ oz) half fat Cheddar cheese, grated, to serve

**1** Bring a pan of water to the boil, add the spaghetti and cook for 6–8 minutes until al dente (tender but still with a slight 'bite').
**2** Meanwhile in another pan, heat the cooking spray, sauté the onion for 3–4 minutes and then add the chilli flakes.
**3** Pour in the chopped tomatoes and cook for 1–2 minutes. Then add the mixed seafood. Stir in the chopped parsley.
**4** When the spaghetti is cooked, drain and add to the seafood mixture. Toss gently to coat the spaghetti with the sauce, check the seasoning and then divide between four pasta bowls. Sprinkle with the grated cheese and serve immediately.

**TOP TIP** If you like your food slightly hotter, just add more chilli flakes.

**VARIATION** This can be made into a more substantial meal by adding 50 g (1¾ oz) of prawns or chopped salami. The **ProPoints** values per serving will be 8 if using prawns or 9 if using salami.

# French sandwich (pan bagnat)

Serves **6**

| **ProPoints** values per recipe | **31** | calories per serving | **205** |

This was created in France for labourers to take out to the fields for lunch.

*Preparation time 10 minutes + 2 hours infusing time*

**6 medium crusty rolls**
**2 tablespoons white wine vinegar or lemon juice**
**2 garlic cloves, crushed**
**4 tomatoes, sliced thinly**
**1 onion**
**2 red peppers, de-seeded and cut into thin strips**
**2 x 200 g cans tuna in brine, drained**
**a large handful of fresh basil, torn coarsely**
**12 black olives, halved (optional)**
**sea salt and freshly ground pepper**

**1** Slice the rolls in half horizontally. Drizzle the vinegar or lemon juice over the cut faces of the bread. Scatter the garlic and seasoning on top.

**2** Arrange the vegetables, tuna, basil and olives, if using, on one half of each roll and then place the other half on top. Wrap the rolls in foil or a clean tea towel. Place a weight, such as a breadboard, on top and leave for at least 2 hours before serving.

**VEGETARIAN OPTION** You could replace the tuna with 200 g (7 oz) of vegetarian low fat cheese. The **ProPoints** values per serving would be 5.

# Lamb koftas

**4** ProPoints value

Makes **10**

| **ProPoints** values per recipe | **41** | calories per serving | **155** |

A great recipe for a summer lunch – skewers of spicy lamb that can be cooked on the barbecue and served with a crunchy zero **ProPoints** value salad.

*Preparation time 15 minutes + 20 minutes chilling l Cooking time 12–15 minutes*

## FOR THE KOFTAS
500 g (1 lb 2 oz) lamb mince

1 egg yolk

100 g (3½ oz) fresh white breadcrumbs

1 onion, chopped

1 tablespoon chopped fresh parsley

½ teaspoon ground cinnamon

1 teaspoon ground cumin

½ teaspoon chilli powder

1 teaspoon turmeric

½ teaspoon ground allspice

## FOR THE TAHINI AND YOGURT SAUCE
150 g (5½ oz) low fat natural yogurt

juice of ½ a lemon

1 tablespoon tahini

2 garlic cloves, crushed

**1** Soak 10 wooden kebab skewers in water for at least 30 minutes.

**2** Place all the kofta ingredients in a food processor and whizz until completely mixed.

**3** Using your hands, form the mixture into balls and squeeze on to the end of the skewers. Place on a plate or tray and cover with cling film. Leave to chill in the fridge for 20 minutes.

**4** In a bowl, mix together the sauce ingredients and place in the fridge until ready to serve.

**5** Heat the grill until quite hot and cook the koftas for about 12–15 minutes, turning quite often to prevent them from burning. If using a barbecue the same applies – keep checking them to prevent burning.

**6** Serve with the tahini and yogurt sauce.

**TOP TIP** Soaking the kebab skewers prevents them from burning when the koftas are cooking.

# Roasted vegetable open lasagne

**8** ProPoints value

Serves **2** V

| | | | | |
|---|---|---|---|---|
| *ProPoints* values per recipe | **16** | calories per serving | **290** | |

This is a cheat's version in which the lasagne does not need any baking. Roast the filling, quickly cook the fresh pasta and assemble. It really is that simple.

*Preparation time 15 minutes l Cooking time 50 minutes*

4 garlic cloves, peeled
2 carrots, peeled and cut into chunks
4 shallots, peeled and halved
1 red and 1 yellow pepper, de-seeded and sliced
1 small aubergine, cut into chunks
low fat cooking spray
8 fresh sage leaves
8 cherry tomatoes on the vine
4 sheets fresh lasagne
a kettleful of boiling water
3 tablespoons green pesto
salt and freshly ground black pepper
basil leaves, to garnish

**1** Preheat the oven to Gas Mark 7/220°C/fan oven 200°C. Place all the vegetables except the sage leaves and tomatoes in a roasting tin, large enough for them to be in one layer. Spray with the cooking spray and roast for 30 minutes, tossing occasionally.

**2** Add the sage leaves and tomatoes and roast for a further 20 minutes until the vegetables are lightly charred. Season.

**3** Meanwhile, cut each lasagne sheet in half and put it in a large dish or pan. Cover the lasagne sheets with boiling water and soak for 5 minutes, then drain thoroughly.

**4** On a plate, layer the lasagne sheets and roasted vegetables, drizzling each layer with pesto. Serve the dish garnished with basil leaves.

**TOP TIP** Line the roasting tin with foil before using – it makes washing up a lot easier. Roast the vegetables the day before, then cool, cover and chill before reheating in the microwave when ready to use.

**VARIATION** Try a springtime roasted vegetable variation using the 4 garlic cloves, 110 g (4 oz) of halved green beans, 110 g (4 oz) of halved asparagus spears, 6 baby carrots and 6 halved spring onions. The *ProPoints* values will remain the same.

# Coronation chicken and pasta salad

10 ProPoints value

Serves **1**

| **ProPoints** values per recipe | **10** | calories per serving | **290** |

This is a great way to use up cooked chicken, particularly from a roast, when it will have the most flavour.

*Preparation and cooking time 15 minutes*

40 g (1½ oz) dried pasta shells

60 g (2 oz) baby sweetcorn, halved

125 g (4½ oz) cooked chicken breast, skin removed

2 tablespoons 0% fat Greek yogurt

1 teaspoon medium curry paste

½ red pepper, de-seeded and sliced

1 tablespoon fresh coriander leaves, chopped

zest of ½ a lemon, grated finely

salt and freshly ground black pepper

2 spring onions, cut into strips, to garnish

**1** Bring a pan of water to the boil, add the pasta and cook for 10–12 minutes or according to the packet instructions, adding the baby sweetcorn for the final 5 minutes of cooking time. Drain and rinse in plenty of cold water.

**2** Cut the chicken into strips or chunks and place in a large bowl. Mix together the yogurt and curry paste with 1 tablespoon of warm water and season.

**3** Add the pasta, baby sweetcorn, red pepper, coriander leaves and lemon zest to the chicken, pour over the yogurt dressing and mix well. Serve sprinkled with spring onions.

**TOP TIP** Fresh herbs have maximum flavour if chopped at the very last minute before using.

# Summer fruit and white chocolate fool

2 ProPoints value

Serves **2 V**

| **ProPoints** values per recipe | **5** | calories per serving | **140** |

A light and delicious fool. The white chocolate is enough to sweeten the fool without having to add any sugar.

*Preparation time 15 minutes + 30 minutes chilling*

300 g can summer fruits in natural juice, drained

25 g (1 oz) white cooking chocolate, broken into pieces

100 g (3½ oz) very low fat plain fromage frais

50 g (1¾ oz) fresh raspberries, to decorate

**1** Purée the summer fruits in a blender.

**2** Meanwhile, melt the white chocolate in a large heatproof bowl over a small saucepan of simmering water. Add to the fruit purée and blend again. Place in a large bowl, fold in the fromage frais and pour into serving glasses or bowls. Serve at once or chill and serve later. Decorate with fresh raspberries.

**TOP TIP** To melt chocolate, place a saucepan of water on the hob and bring to the boil. Reduce the heat until it is gently simmering. Break the chocolate into chunks and place it in a heatproof bowl. Put the bowl over the saucepan of water so that the base does not touch the water. Let the chocolate melt gently.

# Roasted fruits with orange sauce

![ProPoints value 1]

Serves **4 V**

| **ProPoints** values per recipe | **4** | calories per serving | **183** |

A delicious way to serve fruit – the roasting not only softens it but also draws out the flavours.
*Preparation and cooking time 45 minutes*

200 g (7 oz) large strawberries, hulled
2 kiwi fruits, peeled and quartered
1 mango, peeled, stoned and sliced thickly
4 peaches, stoned and quartered
½ teaspoon ground cinnamon
grated zest and juice of an orange
4 passion fruit
200 g (7 oz) low fat natural yogurt, to serve

**1** Preheat the oven to Gas Mark 7/220°C/fan oven 200°C.
**2** Place the first four fruits into a bowl and sprinkle with the ground cinnamon and orange zest, then mix gently.
**3** Pour the fruits into a roasting tray and roast for 30 minutes, turning them gently after 15 minutes.
**4** Place the orange juice in a pan with the juice of the passion fruit – the pips can be sieved out if you wish but it is not necessary. Simmer on a medium heat for 15 minutes until the liquid has reduced slightly.
**5** Serve the roasted fruits with the orange sauce and the low fat yogurt.

# Apple snow

![ProPoints value 0]

Serves **4 V**

| **ProPoints** values per recipe | **2** | calories per serving | **98** |

A light and fluffy fruity dessert that's easy to prepare ahead – and the perfect recipe for using up those windfall apples.
*Preparation time 20 minutes + chilling*

700 g (1 lb 9 oz) cooking apples, peeled, cored and chopped
½ teaspoon ground cinnamon
4 tablespoons artificial sweetener
100 g (3½ oz) low fat natural yogurt
1 egg white
1 dessert apple, cored and sliced

**1** Place the cooking apples in a saucepan with the cinnamon and 2 tablespoons of water. Cover the pan and cook gently for 10 minutes, stirring occasionally, until the apples have softened to a purée. Transfer to a mixing bowl, stir in the sweetener and leave to cool.
**2** Stir the yogurt into the cooled apple purée. Beat the egg white in a clean bowl until it holds soft peaks and then fold it into the apple mixture using a metal spoon. Divide between four dessert dishes, cover with cling film and chill for 1 hour.
**3** Top the apple snow with the sliced apple before serving.

**TOP TIP** When beating egg whites, always start your mixer on a low speed then gradually increase the speed once they are frothy. This creates many small bubbles rather than fewer large ones, giving a more stable structure, which is especially important when making meringue mixture.

# Panna cotta

U 8 ProPoints value

Serves **4**

| **ProPoints** values per recipe | **30** | calories per serving | **98** |

This rich and creamy Italian set custard is an easy and delicious dessert. Top it with caramelised orange sticks for an extra treat.

*Preparation and cooking time 15 minutes + chilling time*

425 ml (15 fl oz) semi skimmed milk
12 g sachet gelatine
110 g (4 oz) caster sugar
4 egg yolks, beaten
finely grated zest of an orange
2 tablespoons half fat crème fraîche

**FOR THE TOPPING**
strips of peel (see Top Tip) from an orange, plus the juice
   (4 tablespoons)
2 teaspoons caster sugar

**1** Place 200 ml (7 fl oz) of the milk in a small pan, warm to just below boiling point, remove from the heat, sprinkle over the gelatine and stir to dissolve.

**2** Mix the remaining milk and sugar in a pan over a low heat, stirring to dissolve the sugar and bring to the boil. Add the egg yolks and, stirring continuously, bring back to the boil. Cook for 1 minute until the mixture coats the back of the spoon. Add the gelatine milk and bring back to just below boiling point. Do not boil. Strain the mixture at this point if it is at all lumpy.

**3** Stir in the orange zest and crème fraîche. Pour into 150 ml (5 fl oz) ramekins and leave to cool. They should set almost immediately, but chill for at least 1 hour before serving.

**4** To make the topping, place the ingredients in a small pan, bring to the boil and simmer for 2–3 minutes until reduced and syrupy. Cool and serve on top of the panna cotta.

**TOP TIP** To make orange strips, use a vegetable peeler or knife to pare the rind, leaving the bitter white pith behind, then cut into thin sticks.

**VARIATION** Try other flavourings such as 1 teaspoon of vanilla extract, 1 teaspoon of finely grated nutmeg or 1 teaspoon of cinnamon.

# Hot peppered pineapple

Serves **4**

| **ProPoints** values per recipe | **3** | calories per serving | **70** |

A deliciously different recipe – pineapple that is blanched with pepper and sugar syrup and then griddled and topped with creamy crème fraîche.
*Preparation time 15 minutes l Cooking time 15 minutes + 30 minutes cooling time*

1 pineapple, peeled, cored and cut into thick half moon slices
2 teaspoons artificial sweetener
¼ teaspoon freshly ground black pepper
75 g (2¾ oz) half fat crème fraîche, to serve

**1** Place the pineapple slices in a medium saucepan with 300ml (10 fl oz) of water, the sweetener and pepper. Bring to the boil and then simmer for 8–10 minutes until the pineapple is tender but not too soft.

**2** Take the pan off the heat and leave the pineapple to cool in the syrup.

**3** Heat a griddle pan until it is really hot and place the pineapple slices on it. Cook briefly on both sides – just enough to colour and slightly char them.

**4** Serve the pineapple with the crème fraîche.

**TOP TIP** If you find that the pineapple is too hot, add slightly less pepper next time.

# Pistachio ice cream

Serves **6**

| **ProPoints** values per recipe | **44** | calories per serving | **140** |

This is a creamy ice cream that is delicately flavoured with pistachio nuts. It makes a great lunchtime treat.

*Preparation and cooking time 20 minutes + freezing time*

**4 egg yolks**
**6 tablespoons caster sugar**
**1 teaspoon cornflour**
**600 ml (20 fl oz) semi skimmed milk**
**110 g (4 oz) pistachio nuts, chopped finely**
**1–2 drops of green colouring (optional)**

**1** In a large bowl, whisk together the egg yolks, sugar and cornflour until pale and creamy.

**2** Pour the milk into a medium sized pan, add the nuts and bring to the boil. Remove from the heat and whisk into the egg mixture. Return to the pan and cook over a low heat for 2–3 minutes until thickened; it should coat the back of the spoon. Stir in the green colouring, if using.

**3** Pour into a freezerproof container and freeze for 2 hours or until semi solid. Remove from the freezer and mash, using a fork to break up large chunks of ice. Return to the freezer and freeze overnight.

**4** Alternatively use an ice cream machine to churn the mixture, then serve immediately or freeze. To serve, remove from the freezer 20 minutes beforehand. Serve two medium sized scoops per person.

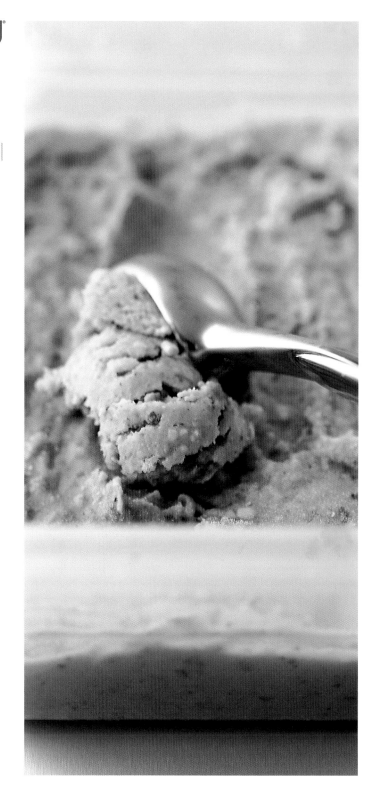

# Potato pizza

10 ProPoints value

Serves **2 V**

| *ProPoints* values per recipe | **21** | calories per serving | **395** |

This pizza is always a hot favourite at dinner parties. Serve in thin wedges as a starter.
*Preparation time 5 minutes l Cooking time 15–20 minutes*

250 g (9 oz) waxy potatoes, peeled, sliced thinly, rinsed and patted dry on kitchen towel
2 garlic cloves, crushed
leaves from a fresh sprig of rosemary
low fat cooking spray
1 large, thin (30 cm/12 inch) fresh pizza base
1 teaspoon plain flour, for dusting
1 teaspoon olive oil
salt and freshly ground black pepper

**1** Preheat the oven to Gas Mark 7/220°C/fan oven 200°C. Put the potatoes, garlic, rosemary and seasoning in a bowl, spray with the cooking spray, toss together then spray again.
**2** Place the pizza base on an baking tray sprayed with the cooking spray and dusted with a little flour.
**3** Spread the potato mixture evenly over the pizza base, drizzle with olive oil and bake for 15–20 minutes until the potatoes are tender and the pizza lightly golden and crisp.

**TOP TIP** This is best made with waxy potato varieties, which include Desirée (the red-skinned potato) and many new and early potatoes such as Pentland Javelin and Maris Piper.

# Cook ahead Deep South stew

6 ProPoints value

Serves **1 V** ❄

| *ProPoints* values per recipe | **6** | calories per serving | **253** |

A rich, warming stew based on the flavours popular in the southern states of America. Serve with fresh greens such as green beans or broccoli.
*Preparation time 15 minutes l Cooking time 15–20 minutes*

low fat cooking spray
1 small onion, sliced finely
1 garlic clove, crushed
50 g (1¾ oz) baby carrots, scrubbed
50 g (1¾ oz) okra or green beans
50 g (1¾ oz) baby sweetcorn
1 tablespoon tomato purée
200 g can chopped tomatoes
½ teaspoon dried chilli flakes
½ teaspoon ground cinnamon
200 g can kidney beans, rinsed and drained
200 ml (7 fl oz) vegetable stock
salt and freshly ground black pepper

**1** Spray a large, lidded, non stick saucepan with the cooking spray and fry the onion and garlic for 5 minutes, adding a little water if they stick, until softened. Add the carrots, okra or green beans, baby sweetcorn, tomato purée, tomatoes, spices, kidney beans, stock and seasoning.
**2** Bring to the boil and then simmer gently with the lid on for 15–20 minutes or until all the vegetables are tender and the sauce is rich and thick.

# For one and two

# French ham and bean casserole

Serves **1**

| **ProPoints** values per recipe | **5** | calories per serving | **327** |

This is a quick and satisfying stew for a cold night. Serve with spinach and mashed potatoes.
*Preparation and cooking time 25 minutes*

low fat cooking spray
1 small onion, chopped finely
1 garlic clove, crushed
200 g can chopped tomatoes
1 teaspoon tomato purée
2 fresh thyme sprigs, woody stems discarded and leaves chopped
½ teaspoon dried oregano or Mediterranean herbs
1 celery stick, sliced finely
1 bay leaf
50 g (1¾ oz) thickly sliced lean ham, cubed
200 g (7 oz) canned haricot beans, rinsed and drained
a small bunch of fresh parsley, chopped
salt and freshly ground black pepper

**1** Spray a non stick frying pan with the cooking spray and fry the onion and garlic for 3 minutes, until softened, adding a tablespoon of water, if necessary, to prevent them from sticking.
**2** Add the tomatoes, tomato purée, thyme, oregano or Mediterranean herbs, celery and bay leaf and bring to the boil. Season and simmer for 5 minutes until thick.
**3** Add the ham and beans and simmer for a further 5 minutes. Stir through the parsley and then serve.

**TOP TIP** To make mashed potatoes, peel some floury potatoes such as King Edward using a potato peeler. Cut the potatoes into small chunks and put them in a saucepan. Cover with cold water. Bring the potatoes to the boil, cover and cook for 25 minutes or until they are tender. Remove any scum on the surface of the water, then drain. Add a few tablespoons of skimmed milk and mash together.

# Fish'n'chips for one

**14** ProPoints value

Serves **1** ❄

| ***ProPoints*** values per recipe | **14** | calories per serving | **455** |

When you fancy fish and chips this recipe is ideal.
*Preparation and cooking time 40 minutes*

175 g (6 oz) potatoes, cut into thin sticks
1 tablespoon sunflower oil
½ teaspoon salt
175 g (6 oz) cod loin
1 teaspoon plain white flour
1 egg white
25 g (1 oz) fresh white breadcrumbs
low fat cooking spray
lemon wedge, to garnish

**1** Preheat the oven to Gas Mark 6/200°C/fan oven 180°C.

**2** Rinse the potato sticks to remove the excess starch and pat dry with kitchen towel. Place in a plastic container with a tight fitting lid. Add the oil and salt. Place the lid on the container and shake thoroughly so all the potatoes get a thin coating of salty oil.

**3** Spread the chips out on a non stick baking tray and bake for 20–25 minutes, until they are golden and crispy.

**4** Meanwhile, rinse the cod loin, pat dry with kitchen towel and then dust it with the flour.

**5** Whisk the egg white until it becomes foamy. Dip the fish into the egg white and then coat it in the breadcrumbs. Lightly spray the crumbed fish with the cooking spray and then place it on a non stick baking tray.

**6** Bake the fish for 15–20 minutes, until it is cooked through and the crumb coating is golden and crunchy.

**7** Serve the fish and chips on a warmed serving plate and garnish with a wedge of lemon.

# Spanish meatballs

**11** ProPoints value

Serves **2** ❄

| ***ProPoints*** values per recipe | **22** | calories per serving | **420** |

These little meatballs are dry fried and cooked in tomato sauce for an easy meal with a Spanish flavour. *Preparation time 15 minutes l Cooking time 25 minutes*

150 g (5½ oz) lean lamb mince
1 small onion, chopped finely
1 garlic clove, crushed
2 teaspoons mixed dried herbs
1 small egg white, beaten lightly
2 tablespoons brandy
100 g (3½ oz) button mushrooms, sliced
300 ml (10 fl oz) passata
1 tablespoon tomato purée
1 teaspoon paprika
150 ml (5 fl oz) hot vegetable stock
100 g (3½ oz) dried spaghetti or other pasta shapes
salt and freshly ground black pepper
chopped fresh parsley, to garnish

**1** In a mixing bowl, combine the lamb, onion, garlic, dried herbs and egg white and season. Using clean hands, form the mixture into small meatballs.

**2** Heat a large, non stick frying pan and add the meatballs, dry frying them until they are lightly browned. Pour in the brandy and let it bubble up for a few moments, then add the mushrooms, passata, tomato purée, paprika and stock. Heat until simmering, then cook gently for 20–25 minutes to reduce the liquid by about one third, stirring occasionally.

**3** About 10 minutes before the end of the cooking time, cook the pasta in plenty of boiling water according to the packet instructions until just tender. Drain thoroughly.

**4** Divide the pasta between two warmed plates and top with the meatballs and sauce. Garnish with plenty of parsley.

# Thai steamed salmon

9 ProPoints value

Serves **2**

| *ProPoints* values per recipe | **18** | calories per serving | **310** |

Steaming times for fish are totally dependent on the thickness rather than the weight, so measure your fish carefully. This Thai-influenced recipe is light yet flavoursome.

*Preparation and cooking time 30 minutes*

low fat cooking spray
4 shallots, sliced finely
2.5 cm (1 inch) fresh root ginger, sliced into fine matchsticks
2 garlic cloves, sliced into fine slivers
25 g (1 oz) soft brown sugar
2 tablespoons fish sauce
2 x 150 g (5½ oz) salmon steaks, each about 3 cm (1¼ inch) thick
fresh coriander, to garnish

**1** Heat a frying pan and spray with the cooking spray. Fry the shallots, ginger and garlic for 1 minute until aromatic, then add the sugar and fish sauce. Stir then set aside.

**2** Place each piece of salmon on the middle of a piece of non stick baking parchment, at least four times its size. Pile the ginger mixture on top of each and then fold up the baking parchment around the fish to make an air tight parcel.

**3** Place both parcels in a steamer, cover and steam for 10 minutes or until the steaks are opaque and cooked through. Serve immediately with the juices poured over and fresh coriander sprigs to garnish.

**TOP TIP** Steam fish either in a fish kettle, bamboo steamer or a saucepan with a steaming basket.

# Hot peppered chicken salad

4 ProPoints value

Serves **2**

| *ProPoints* values per recipe | **9** | calories per serving | **200** |

The contrasting colours of the red skinned apples and the deep green spinach make this a very attractive and appetising dish.

*Preparation time 15 minutes l Cooking time 20 minutes*

2 x 125 g (4½ oz) skinless boneless chicken breasts
1 tablespoon freshly ground mixed pepper
low fat cooking spray
1 red skinned dessert apple (e.g. Braeburn)
1 tablespoon fresh lemon juice
175 g (6 oz) baby spinach leaves
3 tablespoons low fat natural yogurt
1 tablespoon finely chopped fresh chives

**1** Preheat the oven to Gas Mark 6/200°C/fan oven 180°C. Line a baking tray with non stick baking parchment.

**2** Season the chicken breasts generously with the mixed pepper and spray them lightly with the cooking spray. Place the chicken on the prepared baking tray and roast it for 20 minutes.

**3** Core the apple and slice it thinly. Toss it together with the lemon juice and baby spinach leaves and divide the mixture between two plates.

**4** Mix the yogurt with the chives. Slice each chicken breast on the slant – each breast should give 5–6 slices. Pile the slices randomly on top of the spinach and apple. Drizzle with the yogurt and chive dressing, and serve.

**TOP TIP** Add the chicken while it is still warm, this way it begins to just wilt the spinach.

# Steak and ale pie

Serves **1**

| *ProPoints* values per recipe | **10** | calories per serving | **403** |

*Preparation time 25 minutes l Cooking time 50–55 minutes*

low fat cooking spray
1 small onion, chopped finely
1 carrot, peeled and chopped finely
1 celery stick, chopped finely
a sprig of fresh sage, chopped (optional)
100 ml (3½ fl oz) chicken stock
100 g (3½ oz) mushrooms
75 g (2¾ oz) lean sirloin steak, visible fat removed and meat
  cubed
1 teaspoon flour
2 tablespoons ale
salt and freshly ground black pepper

FOR THE PASTRY
50 g (1¾ oz) ready rolled puff pastry
1 teaspoon skimmed milk, to glaze

**1** Heat a non stick saucepan and spray with the cooking spray. Fry the onion, carrot, celery and sage, if using, for 5 minutes or until softened, adding a little stock if necessary to prevent them from sticking.
**2** Add the mushrooms, season and stir fry for a further 2 minutes; then remove all the vegetables to a plate.
**3** Spray the pan again, season and fry the meat until browned all over; then sprinkle with the flour, return the vegetables to the pan and stir it all together.
**4** Pour over the remaining stock and ale and bring to the boil. Reduce the heat, cover and simmer for 30 minutes on a low heat.
**5** Meanwhile, roll out the puff pastry to fit an individual pie dish. Preheat the oven to Gas Mark 4/180°C/fan oven 160°C. Spoon the cooked filling into the dish and lay the pastry on top, pressing down at the edges.
**6** Brush with a little skimmed milk and cut a slit in the middle. Bake for 20–25 minutes or until golden.

# Pesto, Quorn and pepper kebabs

Serves **2 V** ❄

| *ProPoints* values per recipe | **10** | calories per serving | **280** |

*Preparation and cooking time 20 minutes*

225 g (8 oz) Quorn pieces
2 tablespoons pesto
1 red pepper, de-seeded and cut into squares
1 green pepper, de-seeded and cut into squares
1 yellow pepper, de-seeded and cut into squares
2 small red onions, cut into thick wedges
8 bay leaves

**1** Place the Quorn pieces in a bowl with the pesto and mix well.
**2** Thread the pesto-coated Quorn pieces on to four skewers, alternating with squares of pepper, red onion wedges and bay leaves.
**3** Grill for 8–10 minutes, turning frequently, until the vegetables begin to char around the edges. Serve two kebabs per person.

# Mushroom frittata

Serves **1 V**

| *ProPoints* values per recipe | **3** | calories per serving | **142** |

*Preparation and cooking time 25 minutes*

low fat cooking spray
1 garlic clove, chopped finely
250 g (9 oz) mushrooms, sliced
1 lemon wedge
1 egg
1 egg white
a few sprigs of fresh parsley or thyme, chopped
salt and freshly ground black pepper

**1** Heat a small, non stick frying pan and spray with the cooking spray, then stir fry the garlic for a minute until golden. With the heat on high add the mushrooms and stir fry for a minute. Season, then squeeze the lemon wedge over them.
**2** Beat the egg and egg white together with the parsley or thyme in a small bowl until frothy. Then turn down the heat and add to the mushrooms. Cook for 1–2 minutes until the base of the frittata has set.
**3** Preheat the grill to high, brown the top of the frittata and then cut into wedges to serve.

**TOP TIP** To separate an egg, crack a fresh one on the side of the bowl and break the egg shell into two halves, using your thumbs to pull it apart. Over a bowl, gently rock the yolk back and forth between the two halves of shell, allowing the white to slip into the bowl. Continue doing this until the white is out, then place the yolk in a separate bowl.

# Lamb stuffed red peppers

Serves **2**

| **ProPoints** values per recipe | **12** | calories per serving | **285** |

Serve with a zero **ProPoints** value green vegetable such as broccoli and 100 g (3½ oz) new potatoes per person, for 2 extra **ProPoints** values per serving.

*Preparation time 10 minutes l Cooking time 35–45 minutes*

2 large red peppers
low fat cooking spray
1 small onion, chopped
1 teaspoon chopped fresh root ginger
1 garlic clove, crushed
½ teaspoon garam masala
200 g (7 oz) lamb mince
½ green chilli, de-seeded and chopped finely
1 tablespoon chopped fresh coriander
salt and freshly ground black pepper

**1** Preheat the oven to Gas Mark 4/180°C/fan oven 160°C. Halve the peppers, cutting through the stalk. Scoop out the seeds.
**2** Spray an ovenproof dish with the cooking spray and place the peppers in the dish.
**3** Spray a frying pan with the cooking spray and fry the onion until golden.
**4** Lower the heat and add the ginger, garlic, seasoning and garam masala. Stir fry for 2–3 minutes.
**5** Add the lamb mince and fry for about 10–12 minutes. Add the green chilli and chopped fresh coriander and stir fry for another 2–3 minutes.
**6** Spoon the lamb mixture into the red peppers. Bake for 15–20 minutes. Serve immediately.

**TOP TIP** Always wash your hands and the knife you have been using after chopping chillies, and be careful not to touch your eyes until you have done this – it will burn!

**VARIATION** Other coloured peppers or large beefsteak tomatoes could also be used in this recipe – make the filling in the same way and stuff the vegetables before placing in the oven. Tomatoes will take slightly less time to cook. The **ProPoints** values will remain the same.

**VEGETARIAN OPTION** Mix 150 g (5½ oz) cooked couscous with a 5 cm (2 inch) finely chopped piece of cucumber, 2 finely chopped tomatoes and 1 tablespoon of chopped fresh coriander. Use to fill the peppers in step 6. The **ProPoints** values will be reduced to 2 per serving.

# Jamaican potato and beans

Serves **2** V

| *ProPoints* values per recipe | **19** | calories per serving | **375** |

This thick, earthy stew is made by combining delicious flavours that bring sunny Jamaica a little closer during the winter months.
*Preparation time 25 minutes l Cooking time 30 minutes*

**600 ml (1 pint) stock or water**
**100 ml (3½ fl oz) reduced fat coconut milk**
**2 carrots, peeled and cut into 2.5 cm (1 inch) sticks**
**1 green pepper, de-seeded and sliced**
**1 onion, chopped finely**
**1 potato, peeled and diced**
**1 bay leaf**
**2 sprigs fresh thyme**
**2 garlic cloves, chopped**
**1 chilli, de-seeded and chopped**
**1 sweet potato, diced**
**1 parsnip, peeled and cubed**
**400 g can kidney beans, rinsed and drained**
**1 tablespoon soy sauce**
**salt and freshly ground black pepper**

**1** Bring the stock or water and coconut milk to the boil in a large saucepan and simmer for 5 minutes. Add the carrots, pepper and onion. Simmer for 10 minutes.

**2** Add the potato, bay leaf, thyme, garlic and chilli. Simmer for a further 10 minutes then add the sweet potato and parsnip and simmer for 20 minutes more.

**3** When all the vegetables are almost done, add the beans, soy sauce and seasoning and stir well before serving.

**VARIATION** The beans and vegetables can be varied to include whatever zero *ProPoints* value vegetables you have available.

# Fresh tomato and Feta pasta

Serves **1** V

| *ProPoints* values per recipe | **9** | calories per serving | **399** |

A fresh tasting pasta dish that combines all the flavours of the Mediterranean summer.
*Preparation and cooking time 20 minutes*

**200 g (7 oz) small tomatoes on the vine**
**4 garlic cloves, unpeeled**
**60 g (2 oz) dried tagliatelle**
**2 teaspoons balsamic vinegar**
**1 teaspoon olive oil**
**½ teaspoon sugar**
**25 g (1 oz) Feta cheese, cubed**
**a small bunch of fresh basil, torn**
**salt and freshly ground black pepper**

**1** Preheat the oven to Gas Mark 7/220°C/fan oven 200°C and place the tomatoes and garlic on a baking tray. Season and roast for 10–15 minutes.

**2** Meanwhile, bring a pan of water to the boil and cook the tagliatelle for 10–15 minutes or according to the packet instructions. Drain and return to the saucepan.

**3** Add the roasted tomatoes, removing and discarding the vine.

**4** Squeeze the garlic out of the skins and chop the flesh, then add to the tagliatelle with the balsamic vinegar, olive oil, sugar, Feta cheese, basil and seasoning. Toss together and serve immediately.

# Banana split

**U 3 ProPoints value**

Serves **1 V**

| **ProPoints** values per recipe | **3** | calories per serving | **250** |

A quick and easy sweet treat for you to enjoy.
*Preparation time 5 minutes*

**1 small banana, peeled and split lengthways**
**60 g (2 oz) scoop low fat ice cream**
**150 g (5½ oz) fresh strawberries, rinsed, dried and hulled**
**1 teaspoon icing sugar**

**1** Arrange the banana halves in a sundae boat or on a plate then divide the ice cream between them.
**2** Halve the strawberries and scatter over the ice cream, sprinkle with sugar and serve.

# Quick pineapple trifle

**U 3 ProPoints value**

Serves **1 V**

| **ProPoints** values per recipe | **3** | calories per serving | **280** |

This easy recipe is just the thing when you fancy a low **ProPoints** value treat just for yourself.
*Preparation and cooking time 15 minutes*

**2 sponge fingers, crumbled**
**¼ x 227 g can pineapple chunks in natural juice**
**125 g tub low fat custard**

**1** Place the sponge finger crumbs in the base of an individual dish.
**2** Spoon the pineapple (reserving two chunks) and any juice over the crumbs. Leave the dish to stand for 5–10 minutes, so the sponge absorbs the juice.
**3** Top with the custard and then decorate with the reserved pineapple. Chill in the fridge until required.

# Baked nectarines, ricotta and amaretti

**4** ProPoints value

Serves **2 V** ❄

| | | | |
|---|---|---|---|
| **ProPoints** values per recipe | **8** | calories per serving | **205** |

*Preparation time 15 minutes l Baking time 15 minutes*

**2 nectarines, halved and stoned**
**50 g (1¾ oz) ricotta**
**1 teaspoon clear honey**
**25 g (1 oz) amaretti biscuits, crushed**
**1 tablespoon amaretto liqueur**

**1** Preheat the oven to Gas Mark 4/180°C/fan oven 160°C. Place the nectarines, cut halves facing up, on a baking tray.
**2** Beat together the ricotta, honey, amaretti biscuits and amaretto liqueur.
**3** Spoon the ricotta mixture on top of the nectarine halves, pressing down slightly.
**4** Bake the nectarines for 15 minutes. Serve hot.

**TOP TIP** Cut a small slice off the base of each nectarine to stop them wobbling on the baking tray.

# Eton mess

**1** ProPoints value

Serves **2 V**

| | | | |
|---|---|---|---|
| **ProPoints** values per recipe | **3** | calories per serving | **75** |

A fantastically simple recipe – sweet and satisfying and just 1 *ProPoints* value.
*Preparation time 5 minutes*

**1 meringue nest**
**100 ml (3½ fl oz) very low fat natural yogurt**
**150 g (5½ oz) fresh strawberries, sliced or chopped**
**2 passion fruit**

**1** Break up the meringue nest in a medium bowl.
**2** Add the yogurt and strawberries and mix very gently.
**3** Divide the mixture between two glasses.
**4** Cut the passion fruit in half and scrape out the flesh. Strain the flesh through a sieve and pour the juice over the glasses of Eton mess. Serve immediately.

**VARIATIONS** Most fruits can be used for this recipe although summer fruits tend to work best. Try using 125 g (4½ oz) of raspberries instead of the strawberries. The *ProPoints* values will remain the same. If you want to make a creamier version, try using 0% fat Greek yogurt instead. The *ProPoints* values will remain the same.

# Plum crumble

Serves **1 V** ❄

| *ProPoints* values per recipe | **9** | calories per serving | **355** |

The crumble topping for this fruity pudding is quickly made by mixing muesli into melted low fat spread. You then mix in a little grated marzipan.
*Preparation time 10 minutes l Cooking time 25–30 minutes*

2 plums, stoned and sliced
1 tablespoon light muscovado sugar
2 teaspoons low fat spread
2 tablespoons no sugar muesli
15 g (½ oz) marzipan, grated

**TO SERVE**
2 tablespoons low fat natural yogurt
a pinch of ground cinnamon (optional)

**1** Preheat the oven to Gas Mark 5/190°C/fan oven 170°C.
**2** Put the plums in an individual baking dish and scatter half the sugar over them. Bake for 5 minutes while preparing the topping.
**3** Melt the low fat spread in a saucepan, remove from the heat and stir in the muesli, the remaining sugar and the marzipan. Sprinkle the topping over the plums in an even layer.
**4** Bake for about 20–25 minutes, until the plums are tender and the topping is crunchy and golden brown.
**5** Serve with the yogurt, sprinkled with a little ground cinnamon, if using.

**VARIATIONS** This recipe works well with baking apples. Rhubarb could also be used – you may need to add some artificial sweetener as it can be quite tart. The marzipan tastes wonderful, but if you don't like it, or you want to reduce the *ProPoints* values, simply leave it out and deduct 1 *ProPoints* value.

# Tropical mango creams

Serves **2 V** *if using vegetarian cheese and vegetarian fromage frais*

| *ProPoints* values per recipe | **4** | calories per serving | **145** |

A simple recipe that takes only a little more effort than an instant whip to make, contains far less *ProPoints* values and is delicious.
*Preparation time 5 minutes + chilling*

210 g can mango pieces in natural juice, drained
100 g (3½ oz) Quark
pared zest and juice of a lime
4 tablespoons virtually fat free fromage frais

**1** Purée the mango in a food processor then beat into the Quark, lime juice and fromage frais. Spoon into serving dishes and decorate with pared lime zest.
**2** Chill then serve.

**VARIATION** Replace the mango with canned papaya in light syrup. The *ProPoints* values will be 4 per serving.

# Pear bruschetta

Serves **2 V**

| ***ProPoints*** values per recipe | **6** | calories per serving | **120** |

Serve with low fat custard.

*Preparation and cooking time 15 minutes*

**2 x 25 g (1 oz) slices malt bread**
**227 g can pear halves in natural juice, drained and juice**
   **reserved**
**½ teaspoon caster sugar**
**½ teaspoon chopped nuts or flaked almonds**
**1 teaspoon cornflour**
**a big pinch of ground cinnamon**

**1** Lightly toast the bread on one side under a preheated medium grill.
**2** Slice the pear halves and then arrange in a fan-like shape on the untoasted side of each slice of bread. Sprinkle on half the sugar and all of the nuts. Grill under a medium heat until the sugar becomes lightly caramelised and the nuts turn golden.
**3** Meanwhile blend the cornflour with a drop of the reserved juice, then stir in the remaining juice. Bring to the boil (either in a small saucepan or a jug in the microwave) until smooth and thickened. Stir in the remaining sugar and the cinnamon.
**4** Drizzle the warm syrup over the grilled toasts. Serve immediately.

**VARIATION** Fresh ripe dessert pears can be used instead of canned. However, omit the cinnamon syrup and serve with 2 tablespoons of low fat natural yogurt, sprinkled with cinnamon.

# Speedy coq au vin  ⑤ 5 ProPoints value

Serves **4** ❄

| **ProPoints** values per recipe | **21** | calories per serving | **220** |

Serve with mashed potato and green beans (French, of course), adding the extra **ProPoints** values as necessary.

*Preparation time 10 minutes | Cooking time 15 minutes*

½ a kettleful of boiling water
6 shallots, halved
450 g (1 lb) skinless boneless chicken breast, cubed
100 g (3½ oz) lean smoked bacon, diced
200 g (7 oz) button mushrooms
425 ml (15 fl oz) hot chicken stock
150 ml (5 fl oz) full-bodied dry red wine
2 teaspoons Worcestershire sauce
1 tablespoon chopped fresh thyme (or 1 teaspoon dried)
salt and freshly ground black pepper
a few thyme sprigs, to garnish

**1** Pour some boiling water over the shallots, to cover, and leave for 5 minutes. This makes them very easy to peel – and without tears. Meanwhile, dry fry the chicken and bacon in a large, lidded, non stick saucepan for 3 minutes, stirring frequently.
**2** Add the mushrooms and the shallots to the chicken, together with a couple of tablespoons of stock. Cook briskly for 2 minutes, then reduce the heat and pour on the remaining stock and wine.
**3** Stir in the Worcestershire sauce, thyme and a little seasoning to taste. Cover and simmer for 15 minutes. Garnish with thyme sprigs and serve.

# Chilli crab noodles  ⑫ 12 ProPoints value

Serves **2**

| **ProPoints** values per recipe | **24** | calories per serving | **455** |

When time is of the essence, create this tasty dish from start to finish in less than 20 minutes.

*Preparation and cooking time 20 minutes*

150 g (5½ oz) dried vermicelli noodles
a kettleful of boiling water
2 teaspoons sunflower oil
1 small red pepper, de-seeded and sliced thinly
100 g (3½ oz) baby sweetcorn, halved
6 spring onions, sliced
200 g (7 oz) canned white crabmeat, drained
2 tablespoons sweet chilli sauce
2 tablespoons tomato ketchup
1 tablespoon soy sauce
2 tablespoons chopped fresh coriander, to serve

**1** Place the noodles in a bowl and cover them with boiling water. Leave them to stand for 5 minutes and then drain thoroughly.
**2** Meanwhile, heat the oil in a pan and stir fry the red pepper and baby sweetcorn for 2–3 minutes. Add the drained noodles, spring onions, crabmeat, sweet chilli sauce, tomato ketchup and soy sauce and stir fry for 2–3 minutes.
**3** Scatter over the chopped fresh coriander and serve.

**TOP TIPS** Vermicelli noodles can go very soggy if left standing around for too long, so serve this dish immediately and avoid over soaking the noodles – 5 minutes is plenty of time as they are thinner than ordinary noodles.

Canned crabmeat may come wrapped in paper; to drain it remove it from the can and squeeze the excess liquid out gently. Don't squeeze too much or you'll be left with very dry flakes.

# Quick, slow

# Chilli crusted lamb cutlets

Serves **4**

| | | |
|---|---|---|
| *ProPoints* values per recipe | **63** | calories per serving | **505** |

*Preparation and cooking time 25 minutes*

3 large red chillies, de-seeded and chopped
2 spring onions, chopped
3 tablespoons lemon juice
2 tablespoons chopped fresh coriander
8 lamb cutlets
salt and freshly ground black pepper

**FOR THE RAITA**
¼ cucumber, grated
200 g (7 oz) low fat natural yogurt
1 tablespoon chopped fresh mint

**1** Preheat the grill. Whizz the chillies, spring onions, lemon juice and coriander in a food processor until chopped roughly.
**2** Spread the mixture over both sides of the cutlets. Season well. Place the cutlets on a baking tray and cook under a hot grill for 3–4 minutes on each side or until cooked to your liking.
**3** Mix the raita ingredients together and serve with the cutlets.

# Chinese pork parcels

Serves **4**

| **ProPoints** values per recipe | **30** | calories per serving | **315** |

Try this nifty way with pork mince for an economical mid week meal.

*Preparation and cooking time 20 minutes*

100 g (3½ oz) dried easy cook rice

450 g (1 lb) pork mince

2 fresh garlic cloves, chopped, or 2 teaspoons garlic purée

1–2 teaspoons puréed ginger

2 tablespoons soy sauce, plus extra for dipping

4 spring onions, chopped

200 g bag beansprouts

1 large carrot, peeled and grated

freshly ground black pepper

1 Iceberg lettuce, whole leaves separated, to serve

**1** Cook the rice according to the packet instructions.

**2** Dry fry the pork mince in a large frying pan for 5 minutes until lightly coloured and crumbly. Stir in the garlic and ginger and cook for a further 5 minutes to ensure the pork is well done.

**3** Stir in the soy sauce, spring onions, beansprouts, carrot and pepper. Cook for 2–3 minutes.

**4** Drain the rice and stir into the pork. Arrange two whole lettuce leaves on each plate. Divide the mince mixture between them, roll each leaf up and enjoy with additional soy sauce, for dipping.

# Warm potato and mackerel salad

[11 ProPoints value]

Serves **2**

| **ProPoints** values per recipe | **21** | calories per serving | **490** |

Salads served warm or, at the very least, at room temperature, are more flavoursome than when eaten chilled. Try this salad and see.
*Preparation and cooking time 25 minutes*

250 g (9 oz) new potatoes, quartered
200 g (7 oz) French beans, trimmed
½ red onion, sliced into rings
1 celery stick, chopped finely
4 cocktail gherkins in vinegar, drained and halved lengthways
2 teaspoons grated horseradish
150 ml (5 fl oz) 0% fat Greek yogurt
150 g (5½ oz) smoked mackerel fillets, flaked into large pieces
8 cherry tomatoes, whole, or 2 large tomatoes, quartered
Iceberg lettuce leaves
salt and freshly ground black pepper

**1** Bring a pan of water to the boil and cook the potatoes for 10–15 minutes or until tender. Add the green beans 5 minutes before the end. Drain and toss in the onion, celery and gherkins.
**2** Mix the grated horseradish into the yogurt and fold into the potato mixture. Season.
**3** Arrange the mackerel and tomatoes on a bed of crisp lettuce leaves. Spoon over the warm potato salad and serve.

**TOP TIP** Make sure you don't use a creamed horseradish, which has a higher fat content.

**VARIATION** Replace the mackerel with 150 g (5½ oz) canned tuna in brine, drained. The **ProPoints** values per serving will be 5.

# Fusilli and chorizo sausage

[6 ProPoints value]

Serves **1**

| **ProPoints** values per recipe | **6** | calories per serving | **220** |

Chorizo is a slightly spicy Spanish sausage that is available in most supermarkets. Its lovely red colour comes from the paprika used to flavour it.
*Preparation and cooking time 30 minutes*

40 g (1½ oz) dried fusilli
low fat cooking spray
½ onion, sliced
½ green pepper, de-seeded and sliced
25 g (1 oz) chorizo sausage, sliced
2 pepperdew piquante peppers (see Top Tip), drained and halved
salt and freshly ground black pepper
1 tablespoon fresh parsley, chopped, to garnish

**1** Bring a large pan of water to the boil, add the fusilli and cook for 10–12 minutes or according to the packet instructions. Drain and rinse with boiling water.
**2** Spray a frying pan with the cooking spray and heat until sizzling. Add the onion and green pepper and stir fry over a medium heat for 5 minutes until softened. Add the chorizo and continue frying for 2–3 minutes until the sausage is browned.
**3** Toss in the pepperdew peppers and fusilli and heat for 1 minute until the mixture is heated through. Season and serve garnished with the chopped parsley.

**TOP TIP** Peppadew peppers are sweet and spicy pickled peppers from South Africa. They are available in jars in most supermarkets but if you can't find them substitute a canned pimiento. The **ProPoints** values will remain the same.

**VEGETARIAN OPTION** Use 30 g (1¼ oz) chopped vegetarian sausage, which will make the **ProPoints** values 6 per serving.

# Squash and blue cheese risotto

[15 ProPoints value]

Serves **2 V**

| **ProPoints** values per recipe | **30** | calories per serving | **695** |

An interesting array of squashes have been appearing in the supermarkets and farmers' markets over the last couple of years, and they are becoming more fashionable to cook with. This is the ideal recipe for those of you who have yet to try this interesting vegetable.

*Preparation and cooking time 30 minutes*

2 teaspoons olive oil
1 large onion, chopped
2 celery sticks, chopped
450 g (1 lb) winter squash or pumpkin, skinned, de-seeded and cut into 1 cm (½ inch) cubes
200 g (7 oz) dried Italian style easy cook rice or Arborio rice
600 ml (1 pint) hot vegetable or chicken stock
4 fresh sage leaves, torn, or ½ teaspoon dried sage
2 tomatoes, de-seeded and diced
75 g (2¾ oz) low fat soft cheese with garlic and herbs
a handful of chopped fresh parsley
50 g (1¾ oz) blue cheese, crumbled
salt and freshly ground black pepper

**1** Heat the oil in a large saucepan and gently cook the onion and celery until softened. Add the squash or pumpkin and cook for 2 more minutes.
**2** Stir in the rice and add the hot stock. Cover and simmer for 10–15 minutes, until the stock is nearly absorbed.
**3** Stir in the sage, tomatoes, soft cheese and parsley. Season to taste. Divide between individual bowls and crumble over the blue cheese.

**TOP TIPS** Arborio rice is the classic short stubby grain used to give risotto its creamy consistency. It does, however, require more cooking than the Italian style easy cook rice, which is an acceptable 'cheats' version.

Omit the oil and dry fry the vegetables to save 2 **ProPoints** values per serving. Replace the low fat soft cheese with virtually fat free fromage frais and save 1 **ProPoints** value per serving.

# Stilton, garlic and mushroom pizza

Serves **2 V**

| **ProPoints** values per recipe | **15** | calories per serving | **220** |

A creamy onion base topped with garlic mushrooms and oozing with blue cheese – delicious.

*Preparation time 25 minutes l Cooking time 12 minutes*

low fat cooking spray
2 red onions, sliced into rings
23 cm (9 inch) ready made thin and crispy pizza base
250 g (9 oz) button mushrooms, halved
2 garlic cloves, crushed
2 tablespoons fresh thyme leaves or 1 tablespoon dried thyme
40 g (1½ oz) Stilton cheese, crumbled

**1** Spray a frying pan with the cooking spray, heat until hot, add the onions and cook over a medium heat for 10 minutes, stirring occasionally until softened and lightly browned.

**2** Spray a baking tray with the cooking spray. Place the pizza base on the baking tray and top with the onion rings.

**3** Respray the frying pan with the cooking spray and heat until sizzling. Add the mushrooms and cook over a medium heat for 5 minutes until the juices begin to flow. Add the garlic and thyme and continue cooking for 3–4 minutes until the juices have evaporated.

**4** Meanwhile, preheat the oven to Gas Mark 7/220°C/fan oven 200°C. Spread the mushrooms over the onions and top with the cheese. Bake the pizza for 12–15 minutes until golden and bubbling.

**TOP TIP** Adding the garlic after cooking the mushrooms for 5 minutes stops it from burning and becoming bitter.

# Lazy lamb and lentils

Serves **4** V ❄

| **ProPoints** values per recipe | **32** | calories per serving | **260** |

We've called this dish 'lazy' since it needs so little preparation or attention.

*Preparation time 10 minutes l Cooking time 20 minutes*

350 g (12 oz) lean lamb, cut into 2 cm (¾ inch) pieces
1 onion, chopped
2 teaspoons garlic purée
2 teaspoons harissa
100 g (3½ oz) dried red lentils
200 g can chopped tomatoes
300 ml (10 fl oz) hot lamb or chicken stock
2 tablespoons chopped fresh parsley
salt and freshly ground black pepper

**1** Dry fry the lamb in a lidded, non stick pan for 5 minutes, until lightly browned all over.
**2** Add the onion, garlic and harissa and continue to cook for a further 3–4 minutes. Add the lentils, tomatoes and stock. Bring to the boil, then cover and simmer for 20 minutes, or until the lentils are tender and the stock is nearly all absorbed.
**3** Stir in the parsley. Check the seasoning to taste. Serve.

**TOP TIP** Lentils are a great source of protein and can be used in place of some of the meat in recipes. They are also delicious in soups, so it's a good idea to keep a packet of red lentils, which don't need pre-soaking of course, in your store cupboard.

# Red hot pepper pasta

Serves **4** V

| **ProPoints** values per recipe | **34** | calories per serving | **386** |

This pasta dish with a kick is great as an after work supper or for lunch with friends.

*Preparation and cooking time 30 minutes*

250 g (9 oz) spinach, tomato or plain dried pasta shapes
200 g (7 oz) watercress, chopped coarsely
100 g (3½ oz) Feta cheese, crumbled
1 tablespoon pine nut kernels, toasted
salt and freshly ground black pepper

**FOR THE SAUCE**
4 red peppers, halved and de-seeded
2 garlic cloves, crushed
2 tablespoons balsamic vinegar
1–2 small red chillies, de-seeded and chopped finely

**1** Bring a pan of water to the boil and cook the pasta as instructed on the packet, until al dente. Preheat the grill to a high heat.
**2** Meanwhile, to make the sauce, grill the red peppers skin side up until blistered and blackened. Place in a plastic bag and leave until cool enough to handle.
**3** Peel off the charred skin and place the flesh in a liquidiser with the other sauce ingredients. Add a few tablespoons or enough water to enable you to whizz to a smooth purée.
**4** Drain the pasta and return to the pan. Immediately add the sauce and remaining ingredients. Toss, then serve.

# Polenta with garlic mushrooms

**10** ProPoints value

Serves **4 V**

| **ProPoints** values per recipe | **38** | calories per serving | **355** |

Polenta makes an interesting alternative to rice and pasta.

*Preparation and cooking time 40 minutes + 30 minutes setting*

2 vegetable stock cubes, crumbled
350 g (12 oz) dried polenta
2 tablespoons finely chopped fresh chives
25 g (1 oz) Parmesan cheese, grated
low fat cooking spray
450 g (1 lb) open cup mushrooms, halved
2 garlic cloves, chopped finely
salt and freshly ground black pepper
1 tablespoon chopped fresh parsley, to garnish

**1** In a large saucepan, bring 850 ml (1½ pints) water and the crumbled stock cubes to a fast boil. Add the polenta and beat well. Reduce the heat and simmer for 5 minutes, stirring continuously.

**2** Remove the pan from the heat and beat in the chives and Parmesan cheese. Pour the polenta mixture into a 18 x 23 cm (7 x 9 inch) shallow, non stick square tin and allow it to set in the fridge for about 30 minutes.

**3** When the polenta is firm to the touch, turn it out on to a clean board or work surface. Cut it into eight triangles and spray the pieces with the cooking spray. Cook them on a griddle pan for 2–3 minutes on each side until they are warmed through and light brown.

**4** Meanwhile, spray a frying pan with the cooking spray and add the mushrooms and garlic. Season and cook them for 5 minutes, stirring frequently until the mushrooms are tender.

**5** To serve, arrange two triangles of polenta on each serving plate and top with the garlic mushrooms. Garnish with a little chopped parsley.

**TOP TIPS** If you don't own a griddle pan, just grill the polenta triangles under a hot grill for 2–3 minutes on each side.

It is important to keep stirring the pan as you cook the polenta to prevent lumps from forming.

You can make polenta up to 2 days before you need it; keep it well covered in the fridge and griddle portions of it whenever you want.

# Red lentil and aubergine curry

Serves **4 V** ❄

| **ProPoints** values per recipe | **21** | calories per serving | **210** |

The lentils, aubergine and coconut combine beautifully to make a lovely rich sauce.

*Preparation time 25 minutes l Cooking time 30 minutes*

low fat cooking spray

1 onion, chopped

2 garlic cloves, crushed

2 tablespoons medium curry powder

½ teaspoon salt

1 aubergine, diced

175 g (6 oz) dried red lentils

600 ml (20 fl oz) vegetable stock

100 ml (3½ fl oz) reduced fat coconut milk

2 tablespoons chopped fresh coriander

**1** Spray a non stick frying pan with the cooking spray and gently cook the onion and garlic until softened, but not browned. Stir in the curry powder and cook for 1 minute.

**2** Add the salt, aubergine, lentils and stock to the pan. Bring to the boil and simmer uncovered for 30 minutes, stirring regularly to prevent the lentils sticking.

**3** By this time the lentils should be tender and mushy – if not, raise the heat and boil vigorously for 5 minutes. Add the coconut milk and coriander and mix well. Heat through and serve.

**VARIATION** Leave out the coconut milk and stir in 2 tablespoons of tomato purée instead. The **ProPoints** values per serving will remain the same.

# Easy vegetable curry

Serves **4** V ❄

| **ProPoints** values per recipe | **3** | calories per serving | **125** |

*Preparation time 15 minutes l Cooking time 40 minutes*

1 onion, chopped
2 garlic cloves, crushed
175 g (6 oz) carrots, peeled and sliced
225 g (8 oz) leeks, sliced
225 g (8 oz) courgettes, sliced
1 aubergine, diced
350 g (12 oz) cauliflower, broken into florets
100 g (3½ oz) fine green beans, halved
175 g (6 oz) button mushrooms, quartered
2 tablespoons medium curry powder
300 ml (10 fl oz) vegetable stock
400 g can chopped tomatoes
salt and freshly ground black pepper
2 tablespoons chopped fresh coriander, to garnish

**1** Place the onion, garlic, carrots, leeks, courgettes, aubergine, cauliflower, green beans and mushrooms in a large saucepan and add the curry powder. Mix well so that the vegetables become coated with the curry powder.
**2** Stir in the stock and tomatoes and season to taste. Bring to the boil and then simmer, uncovered, for 40 minutes, stirring from time to time.
**3** Serve the curry sprinkled with chopped fresh coriander.

# Hearty beef and beer casserole

Serves **4** ❄

| **ProPoints** values per recipe | **19** | calories per serving | **195** |

A rich and comforting stew that is excellent with steamed leeks and a 225 g (8 oz) baked potato per person, cooked in its skin, for an extra
5 **ProPoints** values per serving.

*Preparation time 30 minutes l Cooking time 1 hour*

low fat cooking spray
400 g (14 oz) lean stewing steak, cubed
2 onions, chopped finely
2 tablespoons plain flour
2 carrots, peeled and sliced finely
4 celery sticks, sliced finely
2 fresh sage sprigs, chopped (optional)
200 g (7 oz) baby button mushrooms, washed
300 ml (10 fl oz) beef stock
150 ml (5 fl oz) beer
salt and freshly ground black pepper

**1** Preheat the oven to Gas Mark 2/150°C/fan oven 130°C. Heat a non stick, flameproof casserole and spray with the cooking spray. Season and fry the beef on a high heat, then add the onions and stir fry for a further 5 minutes. Add the flour and stir to coat the meat.
**2** Add the carrots, celery, sage, if using, mushrooms and seasoning and stir fry together for a minute or two, taking care not to let the flour burn.
**3** Pour over the stock and beer and stir, incorporating any 'stuck' juices into the gravy. Cover and place in the oven for 1 hour, stirring occasionally. If the stew starts to dry out, add a little stock or water.

# Apple and pork braise

Serves **4**

| **ProPoints** values per recipe | **24** | calories per serving | **154** |

This easy dish has a real autumnal feel to it. Serve with mashed or baked potatoes and roasted parsnips.

*Preparation time 30 minutes l Cooking time 25 minutes*

low fat cooking spray

400 g (14 oz) pork leg steaks, trimmed of all visible fat and diced into bite size pieces

2 small onions, chopped

2 garlic cloves, crushed

4 celery sticks, chopped finely

a small bunch of fresh sage, chopped, but reserve a few small whole leaves to garnish

450 g (1 lb) cooking apples, peeled, cored and chopped

300 ml (10 fl oz) vegetable stock

salt and freshly ground black pepper

**1** Heat a large, lidded, non stick frying pan and spray with the cooking spray, then stir fry the pork for a few minutes until browned on all sides.

**2** Add the onions and garlic and stir fry for another 5 minutes, until softened, adding a little water if necessary to prevent them from sticking.

**3** Add the celery, sage, apples, stock and seasoning. Bring to the boil, then cover and simmer for 25 minutes. Serve garnished with the reserved sage leaves.

**TOP TIP** To braise meat, place it in a large frying pan with a little low fat cooking spray on a low temperature. Fry the meat with any 'marinade' ingredients such as garlic and onions, allowing the meat to gently combine with the flavours. Add a little water or liquid and then simmer gently to draw out the flavours.

# Roast chicken with lemon and thyme

**9** ProPoints value

Serves **6**

| **ProPoints** values per recipe | **57** | calories per serving | **180** |

*Preparation time 40 minutes  l Cooking time 1¼ hours to cook*

1 medium chicken, weighing approximately 1.5 kg (3 lb 5 oz)
low fat cooking spray
3 lemons, cut into chunky wedges
2 garlic cloves, crushed
a small bunch of fresh thyme, woody stems removed, chopped
300 ml (10 fl oz) chicken stock
salt and freshly ground black pepper

**1** Preheat the oven to Gas Mark 6/200ºC/fan oven 180ºC. Place the chicken in a roasting tray and spray with the cooking spray. Season and squeeze the juice from the wedges of one lemon over the skin, then place the squeezed lemon shells inside the cavity.

**2** Slide your fingers under the skin of the chicken and smear the crushed garlic with a little of the thyme over the breast meat.

**3** Roast for about 30 minutes, basting frequently with the juices in the tray. Remove from the oven and surround the bird with the remaining lemon wedges and sprinkle with the thyme. Spray with the cooking spray, season and baste with any juices from the chicken, then return to the oven for another 45 minutes, until the chicken is cooked through.

**4** To test if the chicken is cooked, stick a skewer or knife into the meatiest portion of one of the thighs. The juices that run out should be clear rather than bloody.

**5** When cooked, remove the chicken to a carving board, cover with foil and keep warm while you make the gravy.

**6** To make gravy, drain off any excess oil in the tin then place the tin on the hob. Heat until the juices boil, then add the stock.

**7** Scrape up any juices stuck to the tin with a wooden spoon or spatula and boil rapidly for a few minutes until the gravy is reduced a little. Strain the gravy into a jug and serve with the carved meat, garnished with the remaining thyme and the roasted lemon wedges.

# Tuna and broccoli quiche

**9 ProPoints value**

Serves **4** ❄

| **ProPoints** values per recipe | **35** | calories per serving | **395** |

*Preparation time 35 minutes l Cooking time 50 minutes + 20 minutes chilling*

### FOR THE PASTRY
150 g (5½ oz) plain white flour, plus 2 teaspoons for rolling
15 g (½ oz) cornflour
75 g (2¾ oz) low fat spread
a pinch of salt

### FOR THE FILLING
150 g (5½ oz) broccoli florets
185 g can tuna in brine, drained and flaked
2 eggs
300 ml (10 fl oz) skimmed milk
salt and freshly ground black pepper

**1** To make the pastry, sift the flour and cornflour into a mixing bowl. Rub in the low fat spread, using your fingertips, until the mixture resembles fine breadcrumbs. Add a pinch of salt and enough cold water to make a soft dough.

**2** Roll out the pastry on a lightly floured surface and use it to line a 20 cm (8 inch) loose bottomed, fluted flan tin. Chill the pastry in the fridge for 20 minutes.

**3** Preheat the oven to Gas Mark 6/200°C/fan oven 180°C. Line the pastry case with non stick baking parchment and baking beans and bake blind for 10 minutes. Remove the paper and the beans and return the flan tin to the oven for 5 minutes.

**4** Meanwhile, bring a pan of water to the boil and cook the broccoli for 5 minutes. Drain. Arrange the broccoli and the tuna in the partially baked pastry case.

**5** Reduce the oven temperature to Gas Mark 4/180°C/fan oven 160°C. Whisk together the eggs and milk with a little seasoning and pour the mixture over the broccoli and tuna. Put the flan on a baking tray and return it to the oven for 45–50 minutes, until the filling has set. Serve warm or cold.

# Chick pea pilau

U 9 ProPoints value

Serves **4** V ❄

| **ProPoints** values per recipe | **37** | calories per serving | **415** |

*Preparation and cooking time 20 minutes*

low fat cooking spray
1 onion, chopped finely
1 garlic clove, crushed
300 g (10½ oz) dried basmati rice
1 teaspoon cumin seeds
1 teaspoon ground coriander
½ teaspoon mild chilli powder
1 teaspoon paprika
225 g (8 oz) carrots, peeled and diced finely
225 g (8 oz) courgettes, diced
227 g can chopped tomatoes
600 ml (20 fl oz) vegetable stock
410 g can chick peas, rinsed and drained
150 g (5½ oz) baby spinach leaves, rinsed
2 tablespoons chopped fresh coriander
salt and freshly ground black pepper

**1** Spray a large, lidded saucepan with the cooking spray and add the onion and garlic. Stir in the rice, cumin seeds, ground coriander, chilli powder and paprika and cook for 2 minutes.
**2** Stir in the carrots, courgettes, tomatoes and stock and bring to the boil. Cover, reduce the heat and simmer for 10 minutes.
**3** Add the chick peas, spinach, fresh coriander and seasoning and stir well. Cover and cook for a further 2–3 minutes, until the rice is tender and the liquid has been absorbed.

**VARIATION** For a nuttier version, use brown rice instead of basmati. You will need to use an extra 300 ml (10 fl oz) stock and the rice will need 40 minutes cooking time before adding the chick peas, spinach and coriander. The **ProPoints** values will be 10 per serving.

# Grilled chocolate peaches

U 3 ProPoints value

Serves **4** V

| **ProPoints** values per recipe | **11** | calories per serving | **135** |

*Preparation and cooking time 10 minutes*

2 fresh ripe peaches, halved and stoned
50 g (1¾ oz) plain chocolate, broken into pieces
125 g (4½ oz) 0% fat Greek yogurt
4 teaspoons light or dark soft brown sugar

**1** Preheat the grill to high. Place the peach halves in four ramekin dishes, cut side up.
**2** Evenly divide the chocolate and place inside each peach hollow. Spoon on the yogurt to cover the peaches completely. Evenly sprinkle the sugar over the surfaces.
**3** Grill for 4–5 minutes, until the sugar has dissolved and the surfaces are bubbling. Serve immediately.

# Ice cream cookie sandwich

6 ProPoints value

Serves **8 V**

| | | |
|---|---|---|
| **ProPoints** values per recipe | **50** | calories per serving | **222** |

In this typically American dessert, chewy cookies are sandwiched together with low fat ice cream – cool and delicious.

*Preparation time 10 minutes l Cooking time 10 minutes*

75 g (2¾ oz) low fat spread
75 g (2¾ oz) caster sugar
1 egg, beaten
½ teaspoon vanilla extract
110 g (4 oz) plain flour
½ teaspoon baking powder
a pinch of salt
10 g (¼ oz) ground almonds
25 g (1 oz) milk chocolate chips
1 tablespoon skimmed milk

**TO SERVE**
8 x 60 g (2 oz) scoops low fat vanilla ice cream

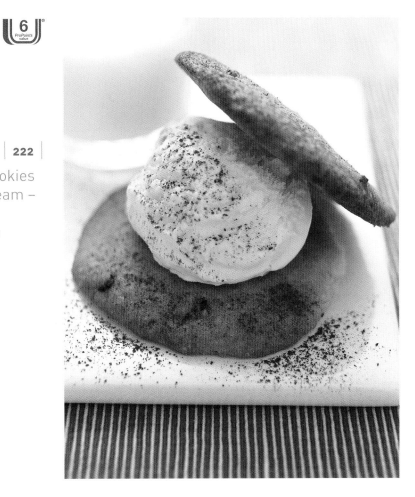

**1** Preheat the oven to Gas Mark 4/180°C/fan oven 160°C. Line two baking trays with non stick baking parchment.
**2** Cream the low fat spread and sugar together until pale and fluffy. Gradually beat in the egg and vanilla extract. Sift the flour, baking powder and salt together and fold into the mixture, followed by the ground almonds, chocolate chips and milk.
**3** Place eight spoonfuls of cookie mixture on each lined tray, leaving room between them to allow for spreading as they cook. Use the back of a spoon to flatten each spoonful into a 6 cm (2½ inch) disc.
**4** Bake for 10–12 minutes until light golden brown. Cool on the baking sheets for 5 minutes then transfer to a cooling rack.
**5** When cold, sandwich pairs of cookies around a scoop of vanilla ice cream and serve immediately.

**TOP TIP** If you want to bake these cookies for the biscuit tin, they work out at 2 **ProPoints** values per cookie.

# Chocolate orange cheesecake

[4] ProPoints value

Serves **10 V** ❄

| **ProPoints** values per recipe | **39** | calories per serving | **162** |

*Cooking time 55 minutes + 2–3 hours cooling*

50 g (1¾ oz) low fat spread, chilled
75 g (2¾ oz) plain flour, sifted with a pinch of sugar, plus extra
    for kneading
low fat cooking spray

**FOR THE FILLING**
50 g (1¾ oz) plain chocolate (70% cocoa solids)
250 g (9 oz) very low fat soft cheese, at room temperature
50 g (1¾ oz) icing sugar, plus 1 teaspoon for dusting
1 tablespoon cornflour
grated zest of an orange
2 eggs

**1** In a mixing bowl, rub the low fat spread into the flour until it resembles breadcrumbs. Gradually add 2 teaspoons of cold water until the mixture starts to hold together. Turn on to a floured board and knead into a ball. Put in a plastic bag and refrigerate for 30 minutes.
**2** Preheat the oven to Gas Mark 4/180°C/fan oven 160°C. Remove the base from a loose bottomed 18 cm (7 inch) cake tin, spray with the cooking spray and then place on a work surface.
**3** Roll and push out the pastry straight on to the base until it is about 5 mm (¼ inch) thick, then reassemble the tin. Cover with foil and scatter with baking beans. Bake for 15 minutes, then remove the foil and baking beans and put back in the oven for 5 minutes.
**4** Melt the chocolate in a heatproof bowl over a small saucepan of simmering water, being careful not to let the water touch the bowl. Beat together the cheese, sugar, cornflour, orange zest and melted chocolate until well blended, then whisk in the eggs.
**5** Pour into the tin. Bake for 35 minutes or until just set. Leave the cheesecake to cool and then turn out and serve.

# Baked chocolate custard pots

[5] ProPoints value

Serves **4 V** ❄

| **ProPoints** values per recipe | **20** | calories per serving | **205** |

*Preparation time 20 minutes l Baking time 1 hour + 2 hours chilling*

a kettleful of boiling water
2 eggs plus 1 egg yolk
300 ml (10 fl oz) skimmed milk
50 g (1¾ oz) plain chocolate (70% cocoa solids)
25 g (1 oz) cocoa powder
25 g (1 oz) caster sugar

**1** Preheat the oven to Gas Mark 2/150°C/fan oven 130°C. Half fill a roasting tin with boiling water.
**2** Place the eggs and egg yolk in a bowl with the milk and beat well. Strain the mixture into a clean saucepan and heat very gently – do not boil, it just needs to get warm. Remove from the heat.
**3** Grate the chocolate over the egg mixture and sift in the cocoa powder. Add the sugar and whisk well.
**4** Pour the chocolate mixture into four individual ramekin dishes. Place the dishes in the roasting tin. Bake in the oven for 1 hour, until the custards have set.
**5** Allow to cool and then chill for 2 hours.

**TOP TIP** Cooking delicate dishes in a water bath, known as a bain marie, spreads the heat so that they cook slowly for a more velvety texture, and prevents them from curdling.

# Baked lemon sponges with sauce

Serves **4 V** ✳ *recommended for the sponges only.*

| *ProPoints* values per recipe | **27** | calories per serving | **235** |

*Preparation time 20 minutes l Cooking time 25 minutes.*

2 eggs
50 g (1¾ oz) caster sugar
100 g (3½ oz) plain flour
finely grated zest of a lemon

**FOR THE SAUCE**
juice of a lemon
2 tablespoons cornflour
25 g (1 oz) fructose
3 tablespoons low fat plain fromage frais

**TO DECORATE**
zest of a lemon (optional)
mint leaves (optional)

**1** Preheat the oven to Gas Mark 4/180°C/fan oven 160°C. Line the base of four individual ramekin dishes with non stick baking parchment.
**2** Using an electric whisk, whisk together the eggs and caster sugar until the mixture is light and foamy. Sift in the plain flour and fold in with the lemon zest.
**3** Divide the sponge mixture between the ramekin dishes and bake for 20 minutes.
**4** To make the sauce, mix the lemon juice and cornflour to form a thin paste. Heat 300 ml (10 fl oz) of water and the fructose in a small pan until boiling. Add the cornflour paste and cook, stirring, until you have a smooth thickened sauce. Reduce the heat and simmer for
5 minutes. Remove from the heat and whisk in the fromage frais.

**5** To serve, run a round bladed knife around the edge of each cooked sponge and carefully remove from the ramekins on to a serving plate. Peel away the baking parchment lining and drizzle over a little of the sauce. Decorate with lemon zest and mint leaves, if using.

**VARIATION** Use an orange or lime instead of the lemon if preferred. You may however need to use 2 limes as they're not as juicy as lemons.

# Apricot and lime sorbet

Serves **4 V** ❄

| **ProPoints** values per recipe | **0** | calories per serving | **25** |

A refreshing dessert on a hot day.

*Preparation time 30 minutes + 5 hours freezing time*

**325 g (11½ oz) ripe apricots, halved and stoned**
**3 tablespoons artificial sweetener**
**juice of ½ a lime**

**1** Place the apricots in a medium pan with 400 ml (14 fl oz) of water and the sweetener. Bring to a simmer and cook for 20–25 minutes until soft.
**2** Leave to cool and then place in a food processor or blender and blend until completely smooth.
**3** Add the lime juice and check for sweetness – more sweetener or lime juice may be added according to your taste.
**4** Place in a plastic sealed container and chill in the freezer. After 2 hours, whisk the mixture around with a fork to break up the ice crystals. Repeat this again after 4 hours.
**5** After 5 hours the sorbet should be ready to serve – frozen but still quite soft.

**TOP TIP** If you forget to whisk the sorbet, or it freezes too hard, just break it up and blend in the food processor to break the ice crystals down again.

# Indian spiced lamb

**10** ProPoints value

## Roasted root cobbler

**8** ProPoints value

Serves **6**

| *ProPoints* values per recipe | **58** | calories per serving | **360** |

This makes a wonderful Sunday lunch for a curry-loving family and is incredibly quick to put together if you have a food processor. Serve with some steamed broccoli.

*Preparation time 10 minutes l Cooking time 1½ hours*

2 onions, grated or minced finely

4 teaspoons grated fresh root ginger

3 garlic cloves, minced

juice of ½ a lemon (about 2 tablespoons)

150 g (5½ oz) 0% fat Greek yogurt

50 g (1¾ oz) ground almonds

250 g jar tikka flavoured spice paste

½ leg lamb (about 900 g/2 lb), extra trimmed

**1** Preheat the oven to Gas Mark 4/180°/fan oven 160°C.

**2** Mix all the ingredients together, except for the lamb, and spread all over the lamb.

**3** Place the lamb on a rack and cook in the preheated oven for 1½ hours.

**4** If the lamb appears to be getting too black, cover with some foil.

**5** Rest the lamb for about 10 minutes before carving into slices. With each slice, serve some of the crisp, spicy outside. Serve three slices for each portion.

Serves **4 V** ✳

| *ProPoints* values per recipe | **34** | calories per serving | **335** |

*Preparation time 25 minutes l Cooking time 50 minutes*

225 g (8 oz) carrots, peeled and cut into chunks

350 g (12 oz) swede, peeled and diced

350 g (12 oz) parsnips, peeled and diced

450 g (1 lb) leeks, sliced

150 ml (5 fl oz) vegetable stock

low fat cooking spray

295 g can low fat condensed vegetable soup

FOR THE COBBLER

150 g (5½ oz) self raising white flour, plus 2 teaspoons for rolling

2 tablespoons chopped fresh parsley and chives

40 g (1½ oz) low fat spread

4 tablespoons low fat natural yogurt

1 tablespoon skimmed milk

a pinch of salt and freshly ground black pepper

**1** Preheat the oven to Gas Mark 5/190°C/fan oven 170°C. Mix together the vegetables and arrange them in a non stick roasting tin. Pour in the stock and spray the vegetables with the cooking spray. Roast in the oven for 25 minutes.

**2** Mix the canned soup with the vegetables and spoon the mixture into an ovenproof dish.

**3** For the cobbler, sift the flour and stir in the herbs and seasoning. Rub in the low fat spread with your fingertips until the mixture resembles fine breadcrumbs. Add the yogurt and enough cold water to make a soft dough.

**4** Roll out the dough on a lightly floured surface to a thickness of 1 cm (½ inch) and stamp out rounds with an 7½ cm (3 inch) cutter. Arrange them around the edge of the dish and brush with the milk. Bake for 20–25 minutes until the topping is risen and golden.

Feed the family

# Mexican beef tacos

**12** ProPoints value

Serves **4** ❄ *for the meat sauce*

| **ProPoints** values per recipe | 47 | calories per serving | 430 |

*Preparation time 15 minutes l Cooking time 15 minutes*

1 large onion, sliced
350 g (12 oz) extra lean beef mince
1 teaspoon harissa or chilli paste
½ teaspoon garlic purée
400 g can red kidney beans, rinsed and drained
400 g can chopped tomatoes with herbs
12 taco shells
salt and freshly ground black pepper
150 ml (5 fl oz) 0% fat Greek yogurt
a handful of fresh coriander
2 limes, quartered, to serve

**1** Place the onion, beef mince, harissa or chilli paste and garlic in a saucepan and dry fry for 5 minutes, stirring frequently. If the mixture becomes too dry, add a few tablespoons of water just to moisten.

**2** Add the red kidney beans and chopped tomatoes. Season well and simmer, uncovered, for 15 minutes.

**3** Heat the grill to high and warm the tacos through for about a minute. Divide the beef mixture between the tacos. Top each one with the yogurt and sprigs of coriander. Serve with a lime wedge.

**TOP TIPS** Taco shells are located in the ethnic section in the supermarket. Mexican ingredients are readily available, and many supermarkets stock their 'own label'.

Serve lots of shredded Iceberg lettuce, tomato wedges and spring onions with these tacos, so that there is plenty to nibble on over this casual meal. Or bulk out the shells with a ready prepared crunchy salad.

# Beef burgers

Serves **4**

| **ProPoints** values per recipe | 19 | calories per serving | 200 |

These home made burgers are easy to make and much more delicious than their shop bought counterparts. Serve on medium burger buns with lots of salad for an extra 4 *ProPoints* values.

*Preparation and cooking time 35 minutes*

250 g (9 oz) extra lean beef mince

2 courgettes, grated

1 carrot, peeled and grated

1 large onion, grated

2 garlic cloves, crushed

1 red pepper, de-seeded and chopped

2 teaspoons English mustard

2 slices bread, made into breadcrumbs

1 egg

low fat cooking spray

salt and freshly ground black pepper

FOR THE SPICY SALSA

½ cucumber, chopped finely

½ small red onion, chopped finely

1 red chilli, de-seeded and chopped finely

½ teaspoon caster sugar

2 tablespoons rice vinegar or white wine vinegar

**1** Mix all the ingredients for the burgers together (except the low fat cooking spray) and then take tablespoons of the mixture and mould into eight burgers.

**2** Spray a frying pan with the cooking spray and fry the burgers in batches for about 3–4 minutes on each side or until cooked through.

**3** Put them on a plate, cover with foil and keep warm while you cook the others.

**4** Meanwhile, make the salsa by mixing all the ingredients together with seasoning.

**5** Serve the burgers with the salsa.

# Sweet and sour prawns

[4 ProPoints value]

Serves **4**

**ProPoints** values per recipe | **18** | calories per serving | **220**

A delicious, low **ProPoints** value version of this popular Chinese dish.

*Preparation time 20 minutes l Cooking time 10 minutes*

110 g (4 oz) dried basmati rice
low fat cooking spray
2 garlic cloves, sliced
2 cm (¾ inch) fresh root ginger, chopped
5 spring onions, chopped into long pieces
1 red pepper, de-seeded and cut into square pieces
250 g (9 oz) raw, peeled tiger prawns
200 g (7 oz) canned water chestnuts

FOR THE SAUCE
100 ml (3½ fl oz) fish stock
3 tablespoons soy sauce
1 tablespoon rice vinegar
1 tablespoon tomato purée
2 teaspoons artificial sweetener
1 teaspoon cornflour, mixed with 3 teaspoons water

**1** Cook the basmati rice according to the packet instructions.
**2** Heat the cooking spray in a wok or large frying pan. Add the garlic, ginger, spring onions and red pepper and stir fry for 4–5 minutes.
**3** Add the prawns and water chestnuts and cook for 1 minute.
**4** Mix together all the sauce ingredients and pour into the wok. Stir fry for 3–4 minutes until the sauce starts to thicken.
**5** Serve with the basmati rice.

TOP TIP Water chestnuts are a sweet, crunchy bulb about the size of a walnut and sold in supermarkets and Chinese grocers.

# Italian pasta salad

[8 ProPoints value]

Serves **4 V**

**ProPoints** values per recipe | **33** | calories per serving | **315**

The home made pesto in this recipe is every bit as tasty as the shop bought version, but it is much lower in **ProPoints** values.

*Preparation and cooking time 20 minutes + chilling*

225 g (8 oz) dried pasta twists
75 g (2¾ oz) stoned black olives
25 g (1 oz) pine nut kernels
15 g (½ oz) fresh basil leaves
1 tablespoon olive oil
1 garlic clove, crushed
2 tablespoons fresh lemon juice
225 g (8 oz) cherry tomatoes, halved
salt and freshly ground black pepper

**1** Bring a pan of water to the boil and cook the pasta according to the packet instructions. This should take about 10 minutes. Drain well.
**2** To make the pesto, place the olives, pine nut kernels, basil leaves, olive oil, garlic, lemon juice and seasoning in a food processor. Blend until all the ingredients are chopped evenly and you have a coarse paste. If you don't have a food processor, you can use a pestle and mortar.
**3** Toss the pesto into the cooked pasta along with the cherry tomatoes. Cover and chill until required.

TIP Toss the pesto with the pasta while it is still warm. The pasta will absorb the flavours better.

# Turkey chow mein

**⑧** ProPoints value

Serves **4**

| ***ProPoints*** values per recipe | **30** | calories per serving | **255** |

A twist on the takeaway favourite – perfect for a Friday night.
*Preparation and cooking time 25 minutes*

**2 teaspoons soy sauce**
**juice of a lime**
**125 g (4½ oz) skinless boneless turkey breasts, cut into thin**
  **strips**
**225 g (8 oz) dried medium egg noodles**
**low fat cooking spray**
**3 garlic cloves, chopped finely**
**50 g (1¾ oz) mange tout, shredded**
**50 g (1¾ oz) ham, shredded**
**3 teaspoons soy sauce**
**6 spring onions, sliced**
**salt and freshly ground black pepper**

**1** Mix together the soy sauce, lime juice and seasoning in a small bowl. Add the turkey strips and leave to marinate for 10 minutes.
**2** Bring a large pan of water to the boil and cook the noodles for 3–5 minutes. Drain and then refresh under cold water. Drain again and reserve.
**3** Heat a wok over a high heat and spray with the cooking spray. Add the turkey strips and stir fry for about 2 minutes then transfer them to a plate. Wipe the wok clean.
**4** Reheat the wok and spray again, then add the garlic and stir fry for 10 seconds before adding the mange tout and ham. Stir fry for 1 minute.
**5** Add the noodles, soy sauce and spring onions and stir fry for 2 minutes.
**6** Return the turkey to the wok and stir fry for another 3–4 minutes until the turkey is cooked. Serve immediately.

# Linguine with ham and peas

**⑧** ProPoints value

Serves **4**

| ***ProPoints*** values per recipe | **33** | calories per serving | **325** |

A tasty and simple dish for all the family.
*Preparation and cooking time 25 minutes*

**225 g (8 oz) dried linguine**
**2 teaspoons olive oil**
**100 g (3½ oz) wafer thin smoked ham, shredded**
**125 g (4½ oz) frozen peas**
**100 g (3½ oz) stoned black olives**
**450 g (1 lb) plum tomatoes, peeled, de-seeded and chopped**
  **finely**
**zest of ½ an orange**
**2 tablespoons chopped fresh flat leaf parsley**
**salt and freshly ground black pepper**

**1** Bring a large pan of water to the boil and cook the pasta for 8–10 minutes or according to the packet instructions. Drain thoroughly and mix with the olive oil.
**2** Place the pasta in a large saucepan and add the ham, peas, black olives, chopped tomatoes, orange zest, parsley and seasoning. Heat through while mixing everything together.
**3** Divide the pasta mixture between four warmed plates and serve immediately.

**TOP TIP** If you are in a hurry, use a can of chopped tomatoes instead of skinning and de-seeding fresh ones.

**VARIATION** Use spaghetti or tagliatelle instead of linguine for this recipe if you prefer.

# Beef, mushroom and potato moussaka

Serves **4**

| **ProPoints** values per recipe | **49** | calories per serving | **485** |

It's worth parboiling the potatoes in this recipe since it drastically reduces the cooking time.

*Preparation time 25 minutes l Cooking time 35 minutes*

low fat cooking spray
500 g (1 lb 2 oz) extra lean beef mince
2 garlic cloves, crushed
200 g (7 oz) mushrooms, chopped
400 g can chopped tomatoes
1 tablespoon tomato purée
600 g (1 lb 5 oz) potatoes, parboiled for 5 minutes and sliced
   thinly
2 eggs, beaten
150 g tub 0% fat Greek yogurt
100 g (3½ oz) half fat Cheddar cheese
salt and freshly ground black pepper

**1** Preheat the oven to Gas Mark 4/180°C/fan oven 160°C.

**2** Using a non stick pan and the cooking spray, brown the beef, garlic and mushrooms.

**3** Add the tomatoes and tomato purée and simmer for 5 minutes. Season to taste.

**4** Put half of this mixture in an ovenproof dish and cover with half of the precooked potatoes.

**5** Repeat with the remaining meat and potatoes.

**6** Beat the eggs, yogurt and cheese together and use this to top the moussaka.

**7** Bake uncovered in the preheated oven for 35 minutes.

VARIATION You can jazz this recipe up so that it is suitable for a supper party by substituting wild mushrooms for the mushrooms in the recipe.

# Chicken lasagne

Serves **4** ❄

| **ProPoints** values per recipe | 41 | calories per serving | 415 |

*Preparation time 45 minutes l Cooking time 25 minutes*

2 teaspoons olive oil
350 g (12 oz) skinless boneless chicken breasts, cut into bite
   size chunks
450 g (1 lb) leeks, sliced thinly
1 garlic clove, crushed
400 g can chopped tomatoes
2 tablespoons tomato purée
1 teaspoon dried basil
150 ml (5 fl oz) boiling water
8 no pre cook lasagne sheets
300 ml (10 fl oz) skimmed milk
25 g (1 oz) cornflour
200 g (7 oz) low fat soft cheese
25 g (1 oz) Parmesan cheese, grated
salt and freshly ground black pepper

**1** Heat the oil in a non stick frying pan and add the chicken, leeks and garlic. Stir fry for 5 minutes until the chicken begins to brown.

**2** Add the chopped tomatoes, tomato purée, basil, seasoning and boiling water. Simmer for 15 minutes.

**3** Preheat the oven to Gas Mark 5/190°C/fan oven 170°C.

**4** Spoon half the chicken and leek mixture into a deep, ovenproof rectangular dish and then arrange four sheets of lasagne on top. Spoon on the remaining chicken mixture and finish with the last four lasagne sheets.

**5** Heat the milk until it is boiling. In a bowl, mix the cornflour to a thin paste with a little cold water. Pour the boiling milk into the bowl and then return this mixture to a clean pan and cook, whisking, until it thickens. Stir in the low fat soft cheese and then pour this cheese sauce over the top of the lasagne sheets.

**6** Sprinkle the surface with the Parmesan cheese and bake in the oven for 25 minutes.

**TOP TIP** Lasagne is always a good standby meal to have at hand. It freezes well, so wrap up any leftovers in individual portions and pop them in the freezer for another day.

**VARIATION** You can use 350 g (12 oz) turkey mince for the filling instead of chopped chicken, if you prefer – it will make this dish a little less expensive. The **ProPoints** values per serving will be 11.

# Sweet pumpkin and peanut curry

**5** ProPoints value

Serves **4 V**

| **ProPoints** values per recipe | **20** | calories per serving | **209** |

Serve this hearty curry with 4 tablespoons of cooked basmati rice, for an extra 6 **ProPoints** values per serving.

*Preparation time 30 minutes l Cooking time 20 minutes to cook*

2 teaspoons vegetable oil

4 garlic cloves, crushed

4 shallots, chopped finely

2 teaspoons red or green Thai curry paste

600 ml (1 pint) vegetable stock

2 lime leaves, torn

2.5 cm (1 inch) fresh root ginger, chopped finely

450 g (1 lb) pumpkin, peeled, de-seeded and cubed

200 g (7 oz) sweet potatoes, peeled and cubed

100 g (3½ oz) mushrooms, sliced

100 ml (3½ fl oz) reduced fat coconut milk

50 g (1¾ oz) roasted peanuts, chopped

3 tablespoons soy sauce

a small bunch of fresh coriander, chopped

**1** Heat the oil in a large, non stick pan and then fry the garlic and shallots for 10 minutes, until softened and golden, adding a little water if necessary to prevent them from sticking.

**2** Add the curry paste and stir fry for 30 seconds. Then add the stock, lime leaves, ginger, pumpkin and sweet potatoes. Bring to the boil and then simmer for 20 minutes or until the potatoes are cooked.

**3** Add the mushrooms and simmer for 5 minutes more before removing from the heat and stirring in the coconut milk, peanuts, soy sauce and coriander. Serve.

TOP TIP To prepare the pumpkin, cut it into wedges and then remove the flesh in large sections with a sharp knife. Alternatively, cut the pumpkin into strips and remove the rind with a potato peeler before cutting into chunks.

# Eggy bread and tomato sandwich

Serves **1**

| **ProPoints** values per recipe | **7** | calories per serving | **305** |

*Preparation and cooking time 15 minutes*

1 egg
4 tablespoons skimmed milk
2 thin slices white bread
1 teaspoon olive oil
1 tomato, sliced
5 basil leaves
salt and freshly ground black pepper

**1** Beat together the egg, milk and seasoning and pour into a shallow bowl. Soak the bread slices in the mixture for 5 minutes until they absorb all the liquid.

**2** Heat the oil in a large, non stick frying pan and add the soaked bread. Cook over a medium heat for 2–3 minutes on each side, until the slices are crisp and golden.

**3** Arrange the tomato slices on one slice of the cooked bread. Scatter the basil leaves over the tomatoes and lightly press the other slice of bread on top. Transfer the sandwich to a serving plate and slice in half.

# Cajun potato wedges

Serves **2 V**

| **ProPoints** values per recipe | **13** | calories per serving | **260** |

Great as a starter or side dish, these crispy spicy wedges are perfectly complemented by the cooling soured cream dip and a zero *ProPoints* value salsa.
*Preparation time 15 minutes l Cooking time 20 minutes.*

2 x 200 g (7 oz) baking potatoes
1 teaspoon Cajun seasoning
low fat cooking spray

**FOR THE SALSA**
10 cherry tomatoes, quartered
½ red pepper, de-seeded and diced finely
½ green chilli, de-seeded and chopped finely
1 shallot, chopped finely
1 teaspoon lemon juice

**FOR THE SOURED CREAM DIP**
150 g (5½ oz) 0% fat Greek yogurt
2 tablespoons sour cream
1 small garlic clove, crushed
1 tablespoon chopped fresh chives
salt and freshly ground black pepper

**1** Preheat the oven to Gas Mark 5/190°C/fan oven 170°C.

**2** Cut each potato into eight wedges then cook in boiling water for 5 minutes. Drain and toss with the Cajun seasoning until evenly coated. Arrange on a baking tray and spray with the cooking spray. Bake for 20 minutes (turning half way through) until crisp and golden brown.

**3** Mix the salsa ingredients together and set aside for 10 minutes to allow the flavours to develop.

**4** Blend together the yogurt, sour cream, garlic, chives and seasoning and serve as a dip for the Cajun wedges.

# Spring vegetable stew

⊍ 5 ProPoints value

Serves **4 V**

| **ProPoints** values per recipe | **19** | calories per serving | **190** |

A fresh tasting spring stew full of cheerful colours and goodness, which is simplicity itself to make.

*Preparation time 2 minutes l Cooking time 20 minutes*

400 g (14 oz) new potatoes
600 ml (20 fl oz) boiling vegetable stock
40 g (1½ oz) pesto sauce from a jar
a bunch of spring onions, chopped roughly
2 garlic cloves, sliced into slivers
200 g (7 oz) sugarsnap peas
200 g (7 oz) runner beans, cut diagonally
200 g (7 oz) baby carrots, scrubbed and halved or quartered lengthways
100 g (3½ oz) frozen petit pois
100 g (3½ oz) frozen, shelled broad beans
a bunch of fresh basil or mint, chopped, to serve

1 Put the potatoes in a saucepan, pour the boiling stock over and boil for 15–20 minutes until just tender.

2 Add the pesto sauce and the rest of the vegetables. Cook for 5 minutes more then serve sprinkled with the basil or mint.

TOP TIPS Pesto sauce is available in jars from the pasta sauce section of supermarkets or it can be bought from the chilled sauces section or delicatessan. Pesto is also good on baked potatoes instead of butter or cheese; spread it sparingly over fish and then grill, or swirl into soup instead of fresh herbs.

VARIATIONS Use red pepper purée, hot harissa paste (1 tablespoon is 1 **ProPoints** value) or tapenade instead of the pesto.

# Fish and chip pie

⊍ 6 ProPoints value

Serves **4**

| **ProPoints** values per recipe | **25** | calories per serving | **230** |

This lovely fish pie has a light golden topping of chipped potatoes – delicious. This is one for all the family to enjoy.

*Preparation time 25 minutes l Cooking time 30 minutes*

370 g (13 oz) cod fillets, skinned
25 g (1 oz) sauce flour
300 ml (30 fl oz) skimmed milk
100 g (3½ oz) peas, cooked
salt and freshly ground black pepper

FOR THE TOPPING
400 g (14 oz) potatoes, parboiled for 5 minutes, cut into matchstick shapes
2 teaspoons lemon juice
2 teaspoons oil

1 Preheat the oven to Gas Mark 6/200°C/fan oven 180°C.
2 Bring a pan of water to the boil and poach or steam the fish for 8–10 minutes, until cooked. Flake, removing any bones.
3 Meanwhile, put the flour and milk in a saucepan and bring to the boil, whilst stirring. When a sauce is formed, simmer very gently for 5 minutes.
4 Mix together the potato, lemon juice and oil for the topping.
5 To assemble the pie, mix together the flaked fish, peas and sauce. Season well. Place in the bottom of a shallow ovenproof dish. Top with the potatoes, season again and bake, uncovered, in the preheated oven, for 30 minutes, until the 'chips' are light brown and crisp.

TOP TIP Sauce flour is now available in all major supermarkets.

# Meringue fruit nests [4 ProPoints value]

Serves **6 V**

| **ProPoints** values per recipe | 26 | calories per serving | 155 |

The meringues are dried out – rather than baked – in a very low heat oven, so be patient. Fill them with fresh fruits for a delicious treat.

*Preparation time 25 minutes l Cooking time 2–3 hours*

3 egg whites
175 g (6 oz) golden caster sugar
1 mango, peeled, stoned and sliced
175 g (6 oz) strawberries, sliced
1 kiwi fruit, peeled and sliced
6 tablespoons low fat aerosol cream

**1** Preheat the oven to Gas Mark 1/140°C/fan oven 120°C. Line two baking trays with non stick baking parchment.
**2** Whisk the egg whites in a grease-free bowl until stiff, gradually whisking in the sugar until the mixture is very glossy and stiff peaks form.
**3** Fit a large piping bag with a star nozzle and fill it with the meringue mixture. Pipe three circles on each baking tray, with diameters of approximately 9 cm (3½ inches) to form the base of the nests. Pipe another layer around the rim of each circle to form the sides of the nests.
**4** Transfer to the oven and bake for 10 minutes, then reduce the oven temperature to Gas Mark ½/120°C/fan oven 100°C. Leave them in the oven for 2–3 hours to dry out.
**5** Remove the meringues from the oven and let them cool down completely before lifting them off the baking parchment.
**6** Mix together the fruit and use to fill the meringue nests. Finish off each one with a tablespoon of aerosol cream.

**TOP TIP** Unfilled meringues will keep for several weeks in an airtight tin.

# Chocolate pudding [11 ProPoints value]

Serves: **4 V** *if using vegetarian crème fraîche*

| **ProPoints** values per recipe | 43 | calories per serving | 355 |

*Preparation time 10 minutes + 30 minutes standing l Cooking time 40 minutes*

1 teaspoon low fat spread
6 thin slices white bread, crusts removed
300 ml (10 fl oz) skimmed milk
170 g can evaporated milk
65 g (2¼ oz) light muscovado sugar
2 tablespoons cocoa powder
1 teaspoon vanilla extract
2 large eggs, beaten

**TO SERVE**
1 teaspoon cocoa powder, for dusting
4 tablespoons half fat crème fraîche

**1** Grease a 1 litre (1¾ pint) baking dish with the low fat spread. Cut the bread into triangles and layer them in the dish.
**2** In a medium saucepan, warm the milk, evaporated milk, sugar, cocoa powder and vanilla extract together, stirring to mix. Do not let the mixture get too hot – you just need to dissolve the sugar and blend in the cocoa powder. Pour in the eggs and whisk the mixture together. Pour this mixture over the bread in the baking dish. Cover and leave to soak for about 30 minutes.
**3** Preheat the oven to Gas Mark 4/180°C/fan oven 160°C.
**4** Remove the covering from the dish and bake the pudding for 35–40 minutes, until set. Cool for a few minutes, then dust with cocoa powder and serve with crème fraîche.

# Jam roly poly

Serves **6 V**

| **ProPoints** values per recipe | 34 | calories per serving | 270 |

This recipe will take you back to your childhood... It's a proper stodgy, steamed version but made with low fat spread rather than suet. The result is well worth the wait.

*Preparation time 25 minutes l Cooking time 1½ hours*

low fat cooking spray
200 g (7 oz) self raising flour
½ teaspoon salt
100 g (3½ oz) low fat spread
6 tablespoons reduced sugar strawberry or raspberry jam
a little skimmed milk, for brushing

**1** Half fill a steamer with water and put on to boil. Spray a piece of foil measuring 23 x 33 cm (9 x 13 inches) with the cooking spray.

**2** In a large bowl, mix the flour, salt and low fat spread together, then add about 7 tablespoons of water and mix to form a light, elastic dough. Knead this very lightly until smooth. Roll out on a floured surface to a 23 x 25 cm (9 x 11 inches) oblong.

**3** Spread the pastry with the jam, leaving a 5 mm (¼ inch) clear border all round. Brush the edges with a little skimmed milk and roll the pastry up evenly, starting from one of the short sides.

**4** Place the roll on the foil and wrap the foil loosely around, to allow for expansion, but seal the edges very well. Place the roll in a steamer (see Top Tip) and cover. Steam over rapidly boiling water for 1½ hours. Remove from the foil and serve.

**TOP TIP** If you do not have a steamer, you can use a large pan with a close fitting lid. You could also cover the pan with foil or baking parchment and then put on the lid so that it is sealed even better. Be sure to keep an eye on the water level and top it up with boiling water if necessary.

# Raspberry tart

Serves **6 V**

| **ProPoints** values per recipe | 15 | calories per serving | 118 |

A light but sophisticated tart that makes a perfect summer dessert for a family lunch or dinner with friends.

*Preparation time 40 minutes + 20 minutes chilling*

**FOR THE PASTRY**
50 g (1¾ oz) low fat spread, chilled
75 g (2¾ oz) plain flour
a pinch of sugar

**FOR THE FILLING**
200 g (7 oz) fresh raspberries
4 teaspoons reduced sugar, high fruit content raspberry jam

**1** Make the pastry by rubbing the low fat spread into the flour and sugar in a mixing bowl until the mixture resembles fresh breadcrumbs. Add 1–2 tablespoons of cold water and bring together quickly with your hand into a ball. Wrap in cling film and chill for 20 minutes.

**2** Preheat the oven to Gas Mark 6/200°C/fan oven 180°C. Roll out the pastry straight on to, and slightly bigger than, the base of a 19 cm (7½ inch) loose bottomed flan or cake tin. Place the base back into the ring, so that the pastry edge comes slightly up the sides. Push into the corners with your fingers and up at the edge. Line with foil or baking parchment and fill with baking beans.

**3** Bake blind for 10 minutes. Remove the beans and lining and bake for a further 10 minutes or until evenly golden brown.

**4** Allow the pastry to cool, then arrange the raspberries on top.

**5** Heat the jam in a small saucepan with 4–5 teaspoons of water and brush over the raspberries to glaze.

# Plum cobbler

Serves **6 V**

| **ProPoints** values per recipe | **31** | calories per serving | **257** |

A cobbler is a rustic, scone-like topping that is used to top a hot fruity dessert, and it makes a pleasant change from crumble. Serve with low fat custard or low fat vanilla ice cream, adding the extra **ProPoints** values.

*Preparation time 15 minutes l Cooking time 25 minutes*

60 g (2 oz) demerara sugar
900 g (2 lb) plums, halved and stoned
½ teaspoon ground cinnamon

FOR THE COBBLER TOPPING
1 tablespoon lemon juice
125 ml (4 fl oz) skimmed milk
175 g (6 oz) plain flour
1 teaspoon baking powder
salt
30 g (1¼ oz) caster sugar
30 g (1¼ oz) low fat spread

**1** Preheat the oven to Gas Mark 5/190°C/fan oven 170°C.
**2** Mix the lemon juice into the skimmed milk and leave to stand for 5 minutes, during which time the milk will curdle – this is normal.
**3** Reserve 1 tablespoon of demerara sugar for the topping, then place the remaining sugar in a pan with the plums, cinnamon and 125 ml (4 fl oz) of water. Cover and simmer for 5 minutes then tip into a baking dish.
**4** Sift the flour, baking powder and a pinch of salt into a mixing bowl. Stir in the caster sugar then rub in the low fat spread until the mixture looks like breadcrumbs. Using a round bladed knife, add the 'soured' milk to bind the cobbler mixture to a soft and slightly sticky dough.

**5** Dollop rough spoonfuls of the cobbler dough on top of the plums, then scatter with the reserved demerara sugar.
**6** Place on a baking tray and bake on the centre shelf of the oven for 25 minutes until the cobbler topping is golden brown and crusty. Leave to stand for 5 minutes before serving.

**VARIATION** To make a rhubarb cobbler, use 750 g (1 lb 10 oz) of chopped rhubarb in place of the plums, increase the sugar to 75 g (2¾ oz) and flavour with ground ginger instead of cinnamon. This will be 6 **ProPoints** values per serving.

# Vanilla rice pudding ⑤ Sticky toffee fruits ③

Serves **4 V**

**ProPoints** values per recipe | 20 | calories per serving | 189

This creamy rice pudding is delicious served hot on its own. Soya milk, now sold widely, is made from yellow soya beans. It has quite a strong flavour and adds a creaminess to recipes such as this. You can use skimmed milk if you prefer, but you will lose some of the creaminess and taste.
*Preparation and cooking time 20–25 minutes*

**700 ml (1¼ pints) soya milk**
**1 vanilla pod, split and scraped**
**low fat cooking spray**
**150 g (5½ oz) risotto rice**
**1½ tablespoons artificial sweetener**

**1** Place the milk and vanilla pod into a small saucepan and place over a medium heat.
**2** Spray a medium pan with the cooking spray and stir in the rice. Cook over a medium heat, whilst stirring, for 2–3 minutes.
**3** Pour a ladle of the milk into the rice and, with the heat slightly higher so the milk bubbles constantly, stir until all the milk is absorbed. Sprinkle in a little of the sweetener with every addition of milk.
**4** Keep repeating this process until all the milk is absorbed and you are left with a creamy vanilla rice pudding.

Serves **2 V**

**ProPoints** values per recipe | 5 | calories per serving | 170

This is a good way to use up over ripe fruit. You can use your favourite fruits in this recipe; pears, plums and pineapple are particularly good, especially served with thick and creamy fat free Greek style yogurt.
*Preparation and cooking time 15 minutes*

**15 g (½ oz) butter**
**juice of an orange**
**1 apple, cored and sliced thickly**
**1 small banana, sliced thickly**
**a pinch of ground cinnamon**
**1 tablespoon soft light brown sugar**

**1** Melt the butter in a frying pan, add the orange juice and apple. Cook for 1 minute, then add the banana and cinnamon. Cook for a further 2 minutes until soft. Remove with a slotted spoon to two serving plates.
**2** Increase the heat and add the sugar. Stir until dissolved and allow the sauce to boil rapidly to reduce and become syrupy. Spoon over the warm fruits. Serve.

# Lime meringue tart

6 ProPoints value

Serves **6 V**

| **ProPoints** values per recipe | **38** | calories per serving | **275** |

This classic tart is traditionally made with lemons, but this lime version gives this old favourite a new lease of life.

*Preparation and cooking time 1 hour + 20 minutes chilling*

### FOR THE PASTRY
**125 g (4½ oz) plain white flour, plus 2 teaspoons for rolling**
**25 g (1 oz) cornflour**
**a pinch of salt**
**75 g (2¾ oz) low fat spread**

### FOR THE FILLING
**3 tablespoons cornflour**
**finely grated zest and juice of 3 limes**
**15 g (½ oz) artificial sweetener**
**2 egg yolks**

### FOR THE MERINGUE
**2 egg whites**
**50 g (1¾ oz) caster sugar**

**1** To make the pastry, sift the flour and cornflour along with the salt into a mixing bowl. Rub in the low fat spread with your fingertips until the mixture resembles fine breadcrumbs. Add enough cold water to mix to a soft dough.

**2** Roll out the pastry on a lightly floured surface and use it to line a 20 cm (8 inch) loose bottomed, fluted flan tin. Chill the pastry in the fridge for 20 minutes.

**3** Preheat the oven to Gas Mark 6/200°C/fan oven 180°C. Line the pastry case with non stick baking parchment and baking beans and bake blind for 10 minutes. Remove the beans and lining paper and return it to the oven for 10 minutes, until the pastry is pale golden and crisp.

**4** Meanwhile, to make the filling, whisk together the cornflour, 150 ml (5 fl oz) of water, the lime zest and lime juice, artificial sweetener and egg yolks. Heat the mixture gently in a small saucepan over a low heat, stirring continuously, until you have a thick sauce.

**5** Spoon the filling into the cooked pastry case and level it with the back of a spoon.

**6** To make the meringue, place the egg whites in a clean mixing bowl and whisk them with electric beaters until stiff. Add the sugar a spoonful at a time and continue whisking until you have a thick, glossy meringue mixture.

**7** Spoon the meringue over the lime filling, using the back of a spoon to swirl it over the top. Return the tart to the oven for 5–8 minutes, until the meringue is golden brown and crisp on top.

**TOP TIP** When baking a pastry case, line it with non stick baking parchment and baking beans. Otherwise the pastry shrinks as it cooks. If you don't have baking beans use dried pulses, such as kidney beans or marrowfat peas.

Comforting classics

# Roast beef with all the trimmings

**15** ProPoints value

Serves **4**

| **ProPoints** values per recipe | **58** | calories per serving | **530** |

Sunday wouldn't be complete without a roast, and this recipe means you can enjoy it without using too many **ProPoints** values.

*Preparation and cooking time 1 hour*

600 g (1 lb 5 oz) beef silverside
salt and freshly ground black pepper

**FOR THE ROAST VEGETABLES**
450 g (1 lb) potatoes, peeled and diced
350 g (12 oz) carrots, peeled and peeled and cut into large
    chunks
225 g (8 oz) small parsnips, cut into quarters
1 tablespoon sunflower oil
1 teaspoon chilli flakes

**FOR THE YORKSHIRE PUDDINGS**
100 g (3½ oz) plain white flour
a pinch of salt
1 egg
300 ml (10 fl oz) skimmed milk
low fat cooking spray

**FOR THE GRAVY**
425 ml (15 fl oz) beef stock
1 teaspoon horseradish sauce
2 tablespoons cornflour

**1** Preheat the oven to Gas Mark 5/190°C/fan oven 170°C. Rinse the beef and place it in a non stick roasting tin. Season well and roast for 1 hour.

**2** Meanwhile, in a large mixing bowl, mix together the vegetables with the oil, a little seasoning and the chilli flakes. After 20 minutes of roasting time, remove the beef from the oven and arrange the vegetables around it. Return the beef and vegetables to the oven.

**3** For the Yorkshire puddings, sift the flour into a mixing bowl and make a well in the centre. Add the salt, egg and milk and whisk to form a smooth batter. Spray a 12 hole, non stick Yorkshire pudding tin with the cooking spray and heat it in the top shelf of the oven for 5 minutes. Carefully remove it from the oven and pour in the batter. Cook on the top shelf of the oven for 20 minutes. Time the Yorkshire puddings so they are ready at the same time as the beef.

**4** When the meat and vegetables are cooked, carefully transfer them to a warmed serving platter. Pour any cooking juices into a small saucepan and skim off any fat. Add the beef stock and horseradish sauce and heat until bubbling. Mix the cornflour with a little cold water to make a thin paste and stir it into the pan. Cook, stirring, until the gravy thickens.

**5** Serve 100 g (3½ oz) of roast beef per person with the Yorkshire puddings, vegetables and gravy.

# Steak, mushroom and Guinness pie

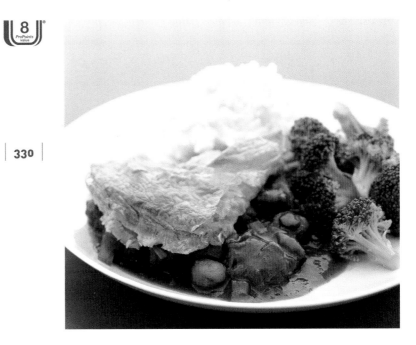

Serves **4**

| **ProPoints** values per recipe | **33** | calories per serving | **330** |

A nostalgic and delicious pie.

*Preparation time 35 minutes l Cooking time 2½ hours*

low fat cooking spray
2 onions, diced finely
1 carrot, peeled and sliced finely
2 celery sticks, sliced finely
2 sprigs fresh sage, chopped
200 g (7 oz) button mushrooms
4 tablespoons plain flour
400 g (14 oz) lean stewing steak, cubed
150 ml (5 fl oz) stock
150 ml (5 fl oz) Guinness
salt and freshly ground black pepper

**FOR THE PASTRY**
100 g (3½ oz) ready rolled puff pastry
a little skimmed milk, for brushing

**1** Preheat the oven to Gas Mark 2/150°C/fan oven 130°C. Heat a non stick frying pan, spray with the cooking spray and fry the onions, carrot, celery and sage until softened. Remove from the heat and put into an lidded, ovenproof casserole dish.

**2** In the same pan fry the mushrooms until softened and add them to the casserole dish.

**3** Sprinkle the flour on a plate, season, then roll the meat in it until completely covered. Spray the pan with the cooking spray again and fry the meat until browned all over. Add to the casserole dish. Pour the stock and Guinness over and put in the oven, covered, for 2 hours, stirring occasionally.

**4** Meanwhile, place a 20 cm (8 inch) pie dish upside down on the rolled out pastry and cut out a circle slightly larger than the dish.

**5** When the meat mixture is cooked, carefully transfer to the pie dish and increase the oven temperature to Gas Mark 7/220°C/fan oven 200°C.

**6** Place the pastry on top of the dish, using any trimmings to make leaves for the top. Push down the pastry on to the edge of the dish to seal and 'knock up' the sides. Brush with a little skimmed milk and make a slit in the middle for the steam to escape.

**7** Bake for 15–20 minutes or until risen and golden.

# Chilli con carne

**7** ProPoints value

Serves **4** ❄

| **ProPoints** values per recipe | **26** | calories per serving | **305** |

*Preparation time 25 minutes l Cooking time 1 hour to cook*

350 g (12 oz) extra lean beef mince
1 tablespoon mild chilli powder
1 teaspoon ground coriander
1 onion, chopped
2 garlic cloves, crushed
175 g (6 oz) carrots, peeled and diced finely
100 g (3½ oz) button mushrooms, quartered
100 ml (3½ fl oz) red wine
400 g can chopped tomatoes
2 tablespoons tomato purée
300 ml (10 fl oz) beef stock
410 g can red kidney beans, rinsed and drained
salt and freshly ground black pepper
2 tablespoons chopped fresh parsley, to garnish

**1** Heat a large, non stick saucepan and add the mince. Dry fry for 2–3 minutes until the mince is browned. Add the chilli powder, ground coriander, onion, garlic, carrots and mushrooms and stir well. Cook, stirring, for 5 minutes.

**2** Pour in the wine, chopped tomatoes, tomato purée and stock, season, stir well and bring to the boil. Reduce the heat and simmer, stirring from time to time, for 1 hour.

**3** About 5 minutes before the end of the cooking time, stir in the kidney beans. Allow them to heat through.

**4** Ladle the chilli con carne into warmed bowls. Sprinkle with chopped fresh parsley and serve.

**TOP TIP** Make this as hot as you want, but take care. Add a little chilli powder first and then taste before adding more – it's worth remembering that the heat of the chilli develops as it cooks.

**VEGETARIAN OPTION** To make a vegetarian version of this chilli con carne, use vegetarian mince and a vegetable stock cube. You'll only need to cook the chilli for 30 minutes. The **ProPoints** values will be 5 per serving.

# Lancashire hotpot

Serves **4** ❄

| **ProPoints** values per recipe | **59** | calories per serving | **480** |

A traditional stew of lamb cutlets with thyme and a crisp and golden potato topping.

*Preparation time 15 minutes l Cooking time 2½ hours*

low fat cooking spray
800 g (1 lb 11oz) potatoes, peeled and sliced thinly
600 g (1 lb 5 oz) lamb cutlets, fat removed and bones cleaned
3 onions, chopped finely
2 carrots, peeled and sliced
4 sprigs fresh thyme, chopped
1 bay leaf
a pinch of sugar
300 ml (10 fl oz) stock
25 g (1 oz) low fat spread, melted
salt and freshly ground black pepper

**1** Preheat the oven to Gas Mark 3/160°C/fan oven 140°C. Spray a casserole or ovenproof dish with the cooking spray then put a layer of potatoes in the bottom. Lay the cutlets on top.

**2** Sprinkle in the onions, carrots and herbs and season well, then sprinkle with sugar. Finish with the rest of the potatoes arranged over the top so that the slices overlap one another.

**3** Pour in the stock and brush the top with the melted low fat spread. Cover and bake for 2½ hours, removing the cover for the last 40 minutes so that the potatoes crisp up and brown.

# Baked lemon spring chicken

Serves **4**

| **ProPoints** values per recipe | **22** | calories per serving | **226** |

A fresh tasting, quick chicken dish. Serve with courgettes and steamed, al dente baby carrots.

*Preparation time 15 minutes l Cooking time 40 minutes*

4 x 165 g (5¾ oz) skinless boneless chicken breasts
4 spring onions, chopped finely
2 garlic cloves, crushed
2 small red chillies, de-seeded and chopped finely (optional)
grated zest and juice of 2 lemons
4 teaspoons olive oil
salt and freshly ground black pepper

**1** Preheat the oven to Gas Mark 4/180°C/fan oven 160°C. Put the chicken fillets in a large baking dish lined with foil. Scatter over the remaining ingredients and fold the foil up to enclose the chicken.

**2** Bake for 40 minutes. Unwrap the foil for the last 10 minutes to allow the chicken to brown.

**TOP TIPS** To keep meat and poultry moist, wrap it in foil, leaving a section open, and place on a baking tray. Scatter over any marinade ingredients you are using. Wrap up the chicken until it is contained in the foil then cook in the oven as required, opening the foil just before the end of cooking to allow the meat to brown. This method seals in the flavour and moisture and does not require any fat for cooking. The same method can be used for fish.

# Club sandwich

Serves **2**

| | | | | |
|---|---|---|---|---|
| *ProPoints* values per recipe | **12** | calories per serving | **405** | |

*Preparation and cooking time 15 minutes*

2 rashers lean back bacon
1 tablespoon low fat mayonnaise
½ teaspoon Dijon mustard
3 medium slices white bread
25 g (1 oz) wafer thin turkey
4 Little Gem lettuce leaves, shredded
1 tomato, sliced
15 g (½ oz) dolcelatte cheese, crumbled
salt and freshly ground black pepper

**1** Grill the bacon and drain it on kitchen towel. Combine the mayonnaise and mustard and spread this on one side of each slice of bread.
**2** Arrange half the turkey on one slice of the bread, top with 2 lettuce leaves, a bacon rasher and half the tomato slices.
**3** Place a second slice of bread on top and then top with the rest of the turkey, bacon, lettuce and tomatoes, cheese and seasoning.
**4** Cover with the last slice of bread, cut into quarters and secure each with a cocktail stick.

# Pizza giardiniera

Serves **2 V**

| | | | | |
|---|---|---|---|---|
| *ProPoints* values per recipe | **17** | calories per serving | **320** | |

This is a 'fresh from the garden' pizza topped with plenty of green vegetables and oozing melted cheese.

*Preparation time 20 minutes l Cooking time 12–15 minutes*

low fat cooking spray
a bunch of spring onions, sliced lengthways
110 g (4 oz) asparagus tips
60 g (2 oz) green beans, halved
60 g (2 oz) peas, defrosted if frozen
2 small courgettes, cut into ribbons (see Top tip)
23 cm (9 inch) thin and crispy pizza base
4 tablespoons tomato purée
6 tablespoons half fat grated Cheddar cheese
1 tablespoon fresh parsley, chopped, to garnish

**1** Preheat the oven to Gas Mark 7/220°C/fan oven 200°C or according to the pizza base packet instructions.
**2** Spray a frying pan with the cooking spray and heat until sizzling. Add the spring onions and cook, stirring, for 3–4 minutes until wilted. Remove from the heat.
**3** Bring a large pan of water to the boil, add the asparagus and beans and cook for 3 minutes. Add the peas and courgettes and cook for a further 2 minutes. Drain thoroughly.
**4** Place the pizza base on a baking tray sprayed with the cooking spray and spread with the tomato purée. Top with the spring onions, vegetables and finally the cheese. Bake for 12–15 minutes until golden and bubbling.
**5** Divide in two and serve garnished with parsley.

TOP TIP Use a vegetable peeler to cut ribbons along the length of the courgettes.

# Persian chicken tagine

Serves **4**

| *ProPoints* values per recipe | **57** | calories per serving | **575** |

A warm cinnamon and cumin flavoured casserole. Serve with 4 tablespoons of cooked rice for an extra 6 *ProPoints* values per serving.
*Preparation time 25 minutes l Cooking time 50 minutes*

low fat cooking spray
680 g (1 lb 9 oz) skinless boneless chicken thighs
1 large onion, chopped
4 garlic cloves, crushed
1 celery stick, chopped finely
2 carrots, peeled and chopped finely
1 tablespoon plain flour
½ teaspoon ground cinnamon
1 teaspoon ground cumin
1 teaspoon ground turmeric
150 ml (5 fl oz) white wine
600 ml (20 fl oz) chicken stock
2 x 400 g cans chick peas, rinsed and drained
a bunch of fresh coriander, chopped
salt and freshly ground black pepper

**1** Heat a lidded casserole or large, lidded, heavy based saucepan on the hob and spray with the cooking spray. Add the chicken thighs, season and brown on all sides, then remove and set aside. Add the onion, garlic, celery and carrots to the pan and cook for 10 minutes, until softened, stirring occasionally.
**2** Mix the flour with the spices and stir in, cooking for 2 minutes. Return the chicken pieces to the pan, pour the wine and stock over, season, cover and cook on a low heat for 45 minutes.
**3** Add the chick peas and cook a further 5 minutes, then sprinkle the coriander over and serve.

# Toad in the hole

Serves **4**

| *ProPoints* values per recipe | **46** | calories per serving | **375** |

The vegetables in this popular dish add a burst of colour. They also make it a more filling meal without adding any *ProPoints* values.
*Preparation time 20 minutes l Cooking time 45 minutes*

1 tablespoon sunflower oil
450 g (1 lb) low fat pork sausages
225 g (8 oz) carrots, peeled and cut into thick chunks
1 red onion, cut into wedges
4 celery sticks, cut into 5 cm (2 inch) pieces

**FOR THE BATTER**
100 g (3½ oz) plain white flour
a pinch of salt
1 egg
300 ml (10 fl oz) skimmed milk
1 teaspoon dried mixed herbs

**1** Preheat the oven to Gas Mark 6/200°C/fan oven 180°C. Place the oil in a 23 cm (9 inch) square, non stick baking tin. Arrange the sausages, carrots, onion and celery in the base of the tin. Roast in the oven for 20 minutes.
**2** Meanwhile, make the batter. Sift the flour and salt into a mixing bowl and make a well in the centre. Add the egg, milk and herbs and whisk to form a smooth batter.
**3** Remove the sausages and vegetables from the oven and pour over the batter. Return the tin to the oven for 20–25 minutes, until the batter is well risen and deep golden.
**4** Cut the toad in the hole into quarters and serve hot.

**VARIATION** Try using other zero *ProPoints* value vegetables for this dish, such as open cup mushrooms or chunks of leeks or courgettes.

# Chicken korma

Serves **4** ✳ *for up to 1 month*

| **ProPoints** values per recipe | **44** | calories per serving | **420** |

A favourite for those who like their curries creamy and not too hot.
*Preparation time 12 minutes l Cooking time 15–20 minutes*

low fat cooking spray
1 onion, chopped
2 garlic cloves, crushed
½ teaspoon chilli powder
½ teaspoon turmeric
½ teaspoon ground coriander
1 teaspoon ground cumin
1 green cardamom pod, crushed
a pinch of salt
500 g (1 lb 2 oz) skinless boneless chicken breasts, cut into bite
　　size pieces
1 teaspoon tomato purée
1 teaspoon grated fresh root ginger
½ teaspoon garam masala
400 ml (14 fl oz) chicken stock
250 g (9 oz) dried basmati rice
100 ml (3½ fl oz) reduced fat coconut milk
25 g (1 oz) flaked almonds
salt and freshly ground black pepper

**1** Heat a medium pan and spray with the cooking spray. Add the onion and garlic and cook for 2–3 minutes.
**2** Add the spices, salt and chicken and stir well to completely coat the chicken.
**3** Add the tomato purée, ginger, garam masala and chicken stock and bring to the boil. Simmer gently for 15 minutes.
**4** Meanwhile, cook the rice according to the packet instructions.
**5** Add the coconut milk and flaked almonds to the chicken mixture and continue to simmer for another 5 minutes. Check the seasoning and serve with the cooked basmati rice.

**VARIATION** For a prawn korma, omit the chicken and use 400 g (14 oz) of prawns instead. The **ProPoints** values per serving will be 10.

# Fish stew with saffron

**2** ProPoints value

Serves **6**

| **ProPoints** values per recipe | **12** | calories per serving | **125** |

A wholesome, tasty fish dish. Serve with a medium crusty brown roll each to soak up the juices – but don't forget to add 4 extra **ProPoints** values per serving.

*Preparation time 15 minutes l Cooking time 12 minutes*

low fat cooking spray
3 shallots, chopped
1 leek, sliced
2 carrots, peeled and diced
2 celery sticks, diced
400 g (14 oz) canned chopped tomatoes
a pinch of saffron threads
600 ml (20 fl oz) hot fish stock
400 g (14 oz) cod fillet, cut into bite size pieces
200 g (7 oz) raw prawns
a bunch of fresh parsley, chopped
salt and freshly ground black pepper

**1** Spray a medium pan with the cooking spray and add the shallots, leek, carrots and celery. Stir fry for 3–4 minutes until starting to soften.

**2** Add the chopped tomatoes and cook for another 2–3 minutes.

**3** Meanwhile, add the saffron threads to the hot fish stock and leave to infuse for 2 minutes.

**4** Pour the saffron infused stock into the pan and add the cod and prawns.

**5** Season and bring to a simmer. Simmer for 4–5 minutes until the prawns turn pink and the cod turns white.

**6** Check the seasoning, stir in the chopped parsley and serve.

# Spaghetti vongole

5 ProPoints value

Serves **4**

| **ProPoints** values per recipe | **21** | calories per serving | **305** |

Vongole is Italian for clams, which are small shellfish available fresh from your fishmonger or ready shelled in brine in most supermarkets. The wine and stock make a great flavoured sauce that clings to the pasta.

*Preparation and cooking time 20 minutes*

**175 g (6 oz) dried spaghetti**
**142 g jar clams in brine**
**50 ml (2 fl oz) dry white wine**
**100 ml (3½ fl oz) fish or vegetable stock**
**2 tablespoons fresh parsley, chopped**
**2 teaspoons crushed dried chilli**
**salt and freshly ground black pepper**

**1** Bring a large pan of water to the boil, add the spaghetti and cook for 10 minutes or 2 minutes less than the packet instructions. Drain and rinse with plenty of boiling water.
**2** Put the clams in a large pan with the white wine and stock and cook for 2 minutes until hot.
**3** Add the spaghetti to the pan with the parsley, chilli and seasoning and cook, stirring over a medium heat for 2 minutes more. Divide between four bowls and serve immediately.

**TOP TIP** By slightly undercooking the pasta initially it will absorb some of the wine and clam juices when you return it to the pan, giving extra flavour to the pasta.

**VARIATIONS** If you can get fresh clams use 450 g (1 lb). To prepare, scrub the clams and discard any that have damaged shells or don't shut when tapped – they are dead. To cook, place them in a large pan with the white wine and stock, bring to the boil and cook for 3 minutes until just opened. Shake the pan occasionally to assist the heat distribution. Add 2 tablespoons of chopped tarragon instead of the parsley for a light aniseed flavour.

# Sweet onion tart

5 ProPoints value

Serves **4 V**

| **ProPoints** values per recipe | **20** | calories per serving | **305** |

Serve with 200 g (7 oz) new potatoes and a crisp green salad, adding on 4 **ProPoints** values per serving.

*Preparation time 15 minutes + 30 minutes cooling l Cooking time 1 hour 10 minutes*

**FOR THE PASTRY**
50 g (1¾ oz) low fat spread
50 g (1¾ oz) plain flour
50 g (1¾ oz) wholemeal flour
a pinch of salt

**FOR THE SWEET ONION FILLING**
low fat cooking spray
1 kg (2 lb 4 oz) onions, sliced very thinly
a small bunch of fresh thyme, chopped
2 eggs
150 ml (5 fl oz) skimmed milk
2 teaspoons French mustard
salt and freshly ground black pepper

**1** Make the pastry by rubbing the low fat spread into the flours and salt until the mixture resembles fresh breadcrumbs. Add about 1 tablespoon of water and mix the dough quickly into a ball with your hand. Wrap in cling film and chill in the refrigerator for 30 minutes.

**2** Meanwhile, heat a large, lidded frying pan and spray with the cooking spray. Add the onions, thyme and seasoning and stir fry for 2 minutes over a high heat.

**3** Cover the pan with a piece of baking parchment tucked down the sides to seal the onion mixture in, then cover with a lid and sweat over the lowest possible heat for 20 minutes. Pull the paper to one side occasionally and stir to make sure the mixture is not sticking to the pan, adding a little water to prevent this if necessary.

**4** Preheat the oven to Gas Mark 5/190°C/fan oven 170°C. Roll the pastry out to a circle about 5 mm (½ inch) thick and use to line a 19 cm (7½ inch) loose bottomed flan tin. Line with foil then fill with baking beans.

**5** Bake for 15 minutes then remove the beans and foil lining and bake for a further 10 minutes or until evenly golden brown.

**6** Meanwhile, beat the eggs with the milk, mustard and seasoning in a jug.

**7** Spoon the cooked onions into the pastry case, pour the egg mixture over and bake for 20 minutes until the filling is set and lightly golden.

**VARIATION** Try filling the tart with roasted zero **ProPoints** value vegetables instead of the onions. The **ProPoints** values will remain the same.

# Aubergine cannelloni

**Serves 4** V *after step 4*

| **ProPoints** values per recipe | **22** | calories per serving | **259** |

There is no pasta in this 'cannelloni' recipe: slices of grilled aubergine are used to lower the *ProPoints* values.

*Preparation time 35 minutes l Cooking time 35 minutes*

100 g (3½ oz) dried long grain rice

2 large aubergines

low fat cooking spray

250 g (9 oz) low fat cottage cheese with onion and chives

a small bunch of fresh parsley, chopped

400 g can chopped tomatoes with herbs

1 onion, chopped finely

2 garlic cloves, chopped finely

a small bunch of fresh basil, leaves removed and larger ones torn

100 g (3½ oz) half fat Cheddar cheese, grated

salt and freshly ground black pepper

**1** Put the rice on to cook as instructed on the packet.

**2** Meanwhile, preheat the grill to high and slice the aubergines into thin slices lengthways. Season and spray with the cooking spray. Grill for 5 minutes on one side, then turn and grill for 2 minutes more until golden.

**3** Preheat the oven to Gas Mark 4/180°C/fan oven 160°C. Drain the rice and mix in a large bowl with the cottage cheese, parsley, seasoning and half the tomatoes.

**4** Spray a non stick frying pan with the cooking spray and fry the onion and garlic for 5 minutes. Add a little water if necessary to prevent them from sticking. Add the rest of the tomatoes and bring to the boil. Simmer for 5 minutes, then season and add the basil.

**5** Place 2–3 tablespoons of the cottage cheese mixture on each aubergine strip and roll up into a cylinder. Place in one layer in a lasagne dish and pour over the tomato and basil sauce. Scatter with the Cheddar cheese.

**6** Bake for 35 minutes, until the Cheddar cheese is golden and bubbling. Allow to stand for a few minutes before serving.

# Apple and blackberry tarts

Serves **6**

| **ProPoints** values per recipe | **25** | calories per serving | **190** |

Make these wonderful, fruit-filled tarts with filo pastry, brushed with a delicately flavoured olive oil rather than butter.

*Preparation and cooking time 25 minutes*

6 x 15 g fresh filo pastry sheets
4 tablespoons light or delicately flavoured olive oil
350 g (12 oz) baking apples, peeled, cored and sliced
1 tablespoon lemon juice
125 g (4½ oz) blackberries
artificial sweetener, to taste

**TO SERVE**
4 tablespoons 0% fat Greek yogurt
2 teaspoons icing sugar
mint or blackberry leaves (optional)

**1** Preheat the oven to Gas Mark 5/190°C/fan oven 170°C.

**2** Unfold the filo pastry sheets and cut the pastry into six piles, measuring approximately 10 cm (4 inches) square. Layer these filo squares in six individual tartlet tins, brushing each pastry sheet with a little olive oil. Pack a little crumpled foil in each tartlet tin and bake for 8–10 minutes until the pastry is golden brown.

**3** Meanwhile, cook the apples in a saucepan with the lemon juice and a couple of tablespoons of water until tender – about 5–6 minutes. Remove from the heat and stir in the blackberries. Cool slightly and then sweeten to taste with the sweetener.

**4** Remove the foil from the filo pastry tarts and spoon in the apple and blackberry filling. Top each one with a tablespoon of Greek yogurt or serve it on the side. Sprinkle with icing sugar and serve, decorated with mint or blackberry leaves, if desired.

**VARIATION** Fill the tarts with soft summer fruits – a mixture of 175 g (6 oz) of strawberries, 175 g (6 oz) of raspberries and 125 g (4½ oz) of blueberries would taste lovely. The **ProPoints** values remain the same.

# Tiramisu

3 ProPoints value

Serves **8 V** ✳

| *ProPoints* values per recipe | **26** | calories per serving | **125** |

Perhaps this dessert has been somewhat over done but that's only because it is so delicious. Here is a low *ProPoints* value version.

*Preparation time 20 minutes + minimum 1 hour chilling*

18 sponge fingers
300 ml (10 fl oz) strong black coffee
200 g (7 oz) virtually fat free fromage frais
150 g (5½ oz) Quark
50 g (1¾ oz) icing sugar
1 teaspoon vanilla essence
25 g (1 oz) cocoa powder
25 g (1 oz) dark chocolate, grated finely

**1** Line the base and sides of a 450 g (1 lb) loaf tin with cling film. Place a layer of sponge fingers in the bottom and pour a third of the coffee over.

**2** Put the rest of the fingers in a separate bowl and pour over the rest of the coffee. Beat half the fromage frais with the Quark, icing sugar and vanilla essence until smooth. Spread half of this mixture over the sponge fingers in the tin.

**3** Sprinkle with a little cocoa powder then top with a layer of the soaked sponge fingers. Spread the remaining half of the cheese mixture over and sprinkle again with cocoa powder.

**4** Top with the remaining sponge fingers, cover with cling film and chill for at least 1 hour. Turn out on to a serving plate and remove the cling film. Spread with the remaining fromage frais and sprinkle with the grated chocolate.

# Mango and berry pavlova

3 ProPoints value

Serves **4–6 V**

| *ProPoints* values per recipe | **11** | calories per serving | **139** |

*Preparation time 15 minutes l Baking time 1 hour*

3 egg whites
4½ tablespoons artificial sweetener
450 g (1 lb) low fat raspberry yogurt
150 g (5½ oz) raspberries
125 g (4½ oz) blueberries
2 mangoes, peeled, stoned and sliced

**1** Preheat the oven to Gas Mark 3/160°C/fan oven 140°C.

**2** Place the egg whites in a completely clean, grease-free bowl and whisk until stiff.

**3** Gradually whisk in the sweetener, 1 tablespoon at a time, until you have a stiff meringue mixture.

**4** Spoon the mixture on to a baking parchment lined baking tray in a circle, with a slight dip in the centre.

**5** Reduce the oven temperature to Gas Mark 1/140°C/fan oven 120°C and bake for 1 hour.

**6** Turn off the oven and leave the pavlova inside until the oven has cooled (baking pavlova just before you go to bed is a good idea, then it can be left in the oven overnight).

**7** When you are ready to serve the pavlova, gently remove the baking parchment and place on a serving plate.

**8** Spoon over the yogurt and top with the fruits. Serve immediately.

# Honey 'ice cream'

ProPoints value 7

Serves **4 V** ❄

| ProPoints values per recipe | 26 | calories per serving | 210 |

This is not really an ice cream as it has no cream in it, but it is so creamy and delicious that no other name fully describes it.

*Preparation time 10 minutes + cooling + minimum 4 hours freezing*

300 ml (10 fl oz) low fat custard made with 2 tablespoons reduced sugar custard powder and 300 ml (10 fl oz) skimmed milk
100 g (3½ oz) clear honey
410 g can 'Light' evaporated milk, chilled

**1** Make up the custard according to the packet instructions but using the honey as the sweetener instead of sugar. Leave to cool.
**2** Whisk the evaporated milk until thick and doubled in volume, then fold into the cool custard mixture with a metal spoon.
**3** Turn into a freezerproof container and freeze until firm around the edges. Whisk with a fork to break up the ice crystals, then freeze again until firm.

**TOP TIP** If you have an ice cream maker then put the mixture into it to freeze; there is no need to whisk to break up the crystals as the machine will do it for you.

**VARIATIONS** For a raspberry, strawberry or mixed summer berry ice, purée 225 g (8 oz) of your chosen berries, fresh, frozen or canned and then fold into the custard. For a ripple effect, only partially fold the berries in at the end to give a swirled pattern. The **ProPoints** values per serving will be 7.

# Baked Alaska

ProPoints value 7

Serves **4 V**

| ProPoints values per recipe | 27 | calories per serving | 150 |

A very impressive and delicious dessert for a dinner party. It looks fantastic and is one of the easiest puddings to make.

*Preparation time 10 minutes l Cooking time 8–10 minutes*

75 g (2¾ oz) sponge flan case
3 egg whites
3 tablespoons sugar
400 ml (14 fl oz) low fat vanilla ice cream

**1** Preheat the oven to Gas Mark 8/230°C/fan oven 210°C.
**2** Place the sponge flan case on a baking tray.
**3** In a clean bowl, whisk the egg whites until stiff, then gradually add the sugar and keep whisking until you have a stiff, glossy mixture.
**4** Quickly spoon the ice cream into the flan case and press into a rounded shape.
**5** Cover the whole flan case and ice cream with meringue and make a pattern of little peaks by patting the meringue with the back of a spoon.
**6** Place in the oven and cook for 8–10 minutes until golden. Keep a close eye on this as it will change from golden to black very quickly.
**7** Serve immediately.

**TOP TIP** When whisking egg whites, the bowl must always be completely grease free or the whites will not stiffen.

Make it special

# Trout stuffed with couscous

12 ProPoints value

## Serves 4

| **ProPoints** values per recipe | 47 | calories per serving | 450 |

A very impressive Moroccan inspired dish, where the couscous and spices are cooked inside the fish. Serve with a fresh, light zero **ProPoints** value salad.

*Preparation time 25 minutes l Cooking time 15–20 minutes*

low fat cooking spray
1 small onion, chopped finely
2 garlic cloves, crushed
1 teaspoon ground cumin
100 g (3½ oz) dried couscous
300 ml (10 fl oz) vegetable stock
1 tablespoon chopped fresh parsley
2 tablespoons chopped fresh mint
4 x 200 g (7 oz) trout, gutted, heads removed and boned
40 g (1½ oz) flaked almonds, chopped
salt and freshly ground black pepper

**1** Preheat the oven to Gas Mark 6/200°C/fan oven 180°C.
**2** Heat a frying pan and spray with the cooking spray. Fry the onion for 2–3 minutes, until softened.
**3** Add the garlic and cumin and cook for 1 minute more.
**4** Add the couscous, vegetable stock and herbs and stir well. Bring to the boil then remove from the heat and leave for 10–15 minutes to allow the couscous to absorb the stock.
**5** Season the trout and fill each one with the couscous.
**6** Place the fish in a shallow baking dish that has been sprayed with the cooking spray. Sprinkle with the chopped almonds.
**7** Bake in the oven for 15–20 minutes until the fish is tender.

# Salmon and asparagus nibbles

2 ProPoints value

## Makes 20

| **ProPoints** values per recipe | 33 | calories per serving | 125 |

These are really tasty canapes to serve at parties, and with 2 **ProPoints** values each you can afford to indulge.

*Preparation and cooking time 10 minutes*

100 g packet asparagus spears, trimmed and halved
10 mini white pitta breads, sliced in half
4 tablespoons tomato purée
250 g (9 oz) low fat cream cheese
zest of a lime, grated finely
75 g (2¾ oz) smoked salmon, cut into thin strips
4 spring onions, chopped finely
salt and freshly ground black pepper
1 lime, cut into wedges, to serve

**1** Preheat the grill to medium. Bring a large pan of water to the boil, add the asparagus spears and cook for 3 minutes until just tender. Drain and rinse with cold water.
**2** Toast the pitta breads under the grill for 2 minutes, turning once until warm. Spread each with a little tomato purée.
**3** Mix the cream cheese with the lime zest and seasoning. Spoon a teaspoon of this mixture onto each pitta half, then top with the smoked salmon and asparagus spears and garnish with spring onions. Serve with lime wedges to squeeze over.

**TOP TIP** Get everything ready before you toast the pitta breads so that you can serve them still warm.

# Duck breasts with pepper sauce

**U** 5 ProPoints value

Serves **4**

| **ProPoints** values per recipe | 21 | calories per serving | 171 |

This wonderfully rich, creamy sauce goes well with succulent duck breasts – for a special occasion. Serve accompanied by zero **ProPoints** value vegetables of your choice.

*Preparation and cooking time 25 minutes*

low fat cooking spray
4 x 125 g (4½ oz), skinless duck breasts, fat removed
1 red onion, diced
2 tablespoons green peppercorns
100 ml (3½ fl oz) chicken stock
4 tablespoons low fat fromage frais

**1** Spray a frying pan with the cooking spray and heat. Cook the duck breasts for 5–6 minutes on each side, depending on how rare you like your meat. Remove from the pan and keep warm.
**2** Add the onion to the pan and cook for 2–3 minutes before adding the remaining ingredients.
**3** Simmer for 3–4 minutes.
**4** Slice the duck breasts and serve with the sauce poured over.

**TOP TIP** To cook duck breast, score the flesh and cook in a pan over a high heat. Cook it until it is slightly pink for a really tender, flavoursome meat. Remember to drain off any fat before serving.

# Prawn cocktail

**U** 3 ProPoints value

Serves **4**

| **ProPoints** values per recipe | 14 | calories per serving | 120 |

Year in, year out, prawn cocktail ranks as one of our all time favourite starters – probably because it tastes so good.

*Preparation time 10 minutes*

6 tablespoons low fat natural yogurt
2 tablespoons tomato ketchup
1 tablespoon tartare sauce
350 g (12 oz) cooked, peeled prawns, defrosted if frozen
a bag of herb salad
1–2 teaspoons seasoned rice vinegar dressing or white wine vinegar
salt and freshly ground black pepper

**TO GARNISH**
1 tablespoon chopped fresh parsley (optional)
1 lime or lemon, sliced into wedges

**1** In a medium bowl, mix together the yogurt, tomato ketchup and tartare sauce. Add the prawns and stir gently to coat. Season.
**2** Toss the salad leaves in the seasoned vinegar dressing or white wine vinegar and then arrange on serving plates. Alternatively, shred the leaves and divide them between four attractive glasses.
**3** Top the salad leaves with the prawn mixture. Garnish with chopped parsley, if using, and lime or lemon wedges and serve.

**VARIATION** For a spicier version, stir ½ teaspoon of de-seeded, finely chopped fresh green chilli and a tablespoon of chopped fresh coriander into the prawn mixture, omitting the parsley. The **ProPoints** values will remain the same.

# Red pepper and basil cheesecake

5 ProPoints value

Serves **6 V** ❄

| | **ProPoints** values per recipe | 28 | calories per serving | 225 |

Not all cheesecakes have to be sweet – try this savoury version and you'll be hooked.

*Preparation time 35 minutes l Cooking time 20 minutes + 10 minutes cooling*

**FOR THE PASTRY**
100 g (3½ oz) plain white flour, plus 2 teaspoons for rolling
1 tablespoon cornflour
50 g (1¾ oz) low fat spread
a pinch of salt

**FOR THE FILLING**
3 red peppers, de-seeded and halved
350 g (12 oz) low fat plain cottage cheese
2 eggs
2 tablespoons torn fresh basil
salt and freshly ground black pepper

**1** To make the pastry, mix the flour and cornflour together in a bowl. Rub in the low fat spread with your fingertips until the mixture resembles fine breadcrumbs. Add the salt and then stir in enough cold water to make a soft dough.

**2** Preheat the oven to Gas Mark 5/190°C/fan oven 170°C. On a lightly floured surface, roll out the pastry so it is big enough to line the base and sides of a 20 cm (8 inch) fluted, loose bottomed flan tin.

**3** Lift the pastry into the tin and prick the base with a fork. Line with non stick baking parchment and baking beans. Bake blind for 10 minutes. Remove the paper and the beans and return the pastry to the oven for 10 minutes.

**4** Meanwhile, grill the peppers under a high heat, skin side up, until the skins blacken and blister. Transfer the peppers to a plastic bag and seal. When they are cool enough to handle, peel off the skins and roughly chop the flesh.

**5** Place the peppers, cottage cheese, eggs, basil and seasoning in a food processor and blend until smooth. Remove the pastry flan case from the oven and spoon in the pepper filling.

**6** Return the flan to the oven for 20 minutes, until the filling has set and is firm to the touch. Allow to cool for 10 minutes before slicing into wedges to serve.

TOP TIP  If you don't have a food processor, chop the red pepper very finely and push the cottage cheese through a sieve. Mix them together with the eggs, seasoning and basil as in step 5 before spooning into the flan case.

# Malaysian BBQ pork

Serves **6**

| **ProPoints** values per recipe | **41** | calories per serving | **225** |

Serve with very lightly steamed pak choi or spinach.

*Preparation time 25 minutes + a minimum of 2 hours marinating l Cooking time 45 minutes*

900 g (2 lb) lean pork fillet, trimmed of all visible fat
2 spring onions, chopped, to garnish

FOR THE MARINADE
1 tablespoon clear honey
150 ml (5 fl oz) dark soy sauce
50 ml (2 fl oz) medium dry sherry
150 ml (5 fl oz) stock
1 tablespoon soft brown sugar
1 cm (½ inch) fresh root ginger, sliced finely
1 small onion, chopped

1  Mix all the marinade ingredients together in a pan. Bring to the boil then simmer for 15 minutes. Let cool.

2  Put the pork fillets in a shallow dish that is large enough to hold them side by side. Pour the marinade over. Cover and chill in the refrigerator for at least 2 hours, preferably overnight, turning the meat several times.

3  Preheat the oven to Gas Mark 6/200°C/fan oven 180°C. Drain the pork, reserving the marinade. Place the meat with the marinated onion and ginger bits on top of it on a rack over a roasting tin and pour water into the tin to a depth of 1 cm (½ inch).

4  Place the tin in the oven and roast for 20 minutes. Remove the meat from the oven and brush with some of the marinade, then put back and roast for another 20 minutes or until cooked through.

5  Meanwhile, put the remaining marinade into a saucepan, bring to the boil then simmer for 5 minutes. Serve the pork in slices either hot or cold with the marinade as a sauce and garnished with chopped spring onions.

# Moroccan spiced rice with lamb

**10** ProPoints value

## Serves 4

**ProPoints** values per recipe | 42 | calories per serving | 430

With the authentic combination of ginger, cinnamon and mint, this Moroccan dish is absolutely delicious.
*Preparation time 30 minutes l Cooking time 20 minutes*

350 g (12 oz) lean lamb mince
1 onion, sliced
2 garlic cloves, crushed
½ teaspoon ground ginger
½ teaspoon ground cinnamon
1 teaspoon paprika
1 aubergine, diced
225 g (8 oz) courgettes, diced
225 g (8 oz) dried long grain white rice
400 ml (14 fl oz) lamb stock
450 g (1 lb) plum tomatoes, skinned, de-seeded and diced
2 tablespoons chopped fresh mint, plus a few extra leaves, to garnish

1 Heat a heavy based, non stick frying pan and add the lamb mince. Dry fry for 5 minutes, draining off any excess fat. Add the onion, garlic, ginger, cinnamon and paprika and stir well.
2 Add the aubergine, courgettes, rice and stock and bring to the boil. Cover and simmer for 20 minutes until the stock has been absorbed and the rice is tender.
3 Add the tomatoes and mint and heat through. Spoon the mixture into a warmed serving dish and scatter with a few extra mint leaves.

TOP TIP The easiest way to skin tomatoes is to plunge them into boiling water for a few seconds – the skins will then peel off easily.

# Sage and orange turkey escalopes

**5** ProPoints value

## Serves 4

**ProPoints** values per recipe | 21 | calories per serving | 235

*Preparation time 15 minutes l Cooking time 30 minutes*

4 x 150 g (5½ oz) turkey escalopes
low fat cooking spray
1 red onion, cut into thin wedges
300 ml (10 fl oz) fresh orange juice
1 tablespoon wholegrain mustard
½ teaspoon dried sage
150 ml (5 fl oz) chicken stock
1 orange, sliced
1 tablespoon cornflour
salt and freshly ground black pepper

1 Season the turkey escalopes on both sides.
2 Heat a large, lidded, non stick frying pan and spray it with the cooking spray. Add the turkey to the pan and cook for 2–3 minutes on each side, until lightly browned. Add the onion wedges to the pan and cook for a further 2 minutes.
3 Add the orange juice, mustard, sage and chicken stock. Arrange the orange slices over the escalopes and bring the liquid to the boil. Reduce the heat, cover and cook for 20 minutes.
4 Mix the cornflour to a thin paste with a little cold water and stir this into the pan. Cook, stirring, until the sauce thickens a little. Transfer the escalopes to warmed plates and spoon the sauce over them to serve.

TOP TIP If you have difficulty finding turkey escalopes, try using turkey breast steaks instead, but hammer them flat with the flat end of a rolling pin. The **ProPoints** values will remain the same. Use juice from freshly squeezed oranges if you can for this recipe.

# Thai beef salad

**2** ProPoints value

## Thai prawn parcels

**1** ProPoints value

Serves **8**

| ProPoints values per recipe | 18 | calories per serving | 135 |

A warm salad with a touch of spice. This is a great lunch party dish.

*Preparation time 15 minutes l Cooking time 5 minutes*

low fat cooking spray
500 g (1 lb 2 oz) lean beef fillet steak, cut into strips
2 garlic cloves, chopped finely
2 cm (¾ inch) fresh root ginger, chopped finely
1 green chilli, de-seeded and chopped finely
juice of a lemon
1 tablespoon fish sauce (nam pla)
2 x 300 g (10½ oz) ripe mangoes, peeled, stoned and chopped
½ large cucumber, cut into strips
100 g (3½ oz) beansprouts
1 Iceburg lettuce, shredded

**1** Heat a wok or large frying pan and spray with the cooking spray. Add the steak, garlic, ginger and chilli and stir fry over a high heat for 3–4 minutes.

**2** Pour in the lemon juice and fish sauce and continue to stir fry until the juices are sizzling.

**3** Remove from the heat and lift out the steak with a slotted spoon. Place in a bowl with the remaining ingredients and toss together.

**4** Place on a large platter and pour over the liquid from the wok.

VARIATION Try replacing the beef with the same quantity of prawns. The **ProPoints** value will be 1 per serving.

Makes **10**

| ProPoints values per recipe | 14 | calories per parcel | 60 |

These parcels are a delicious, savoury treat. They're really easy to do and only 1 *ProPoints* value each.

*Preparation time 20 minutes l Cooking time 15 minutes*

200 g (7 oz) prawns
2 tablespoons fresh chopped coriander
125 g (4½ oz) filo pastry
low fat cooking spray
1 tablespoon red Thai curry paste
salt and freshly ground black pepper

**1** Place the prawns, coriander and seasoning in a blender or food processor and blend briefly until coarsely chopped. Preheat the oven to Gas Mark 6/200°C/fan oven 180°C.

**2** Cut the pastry into squares measuring roughly 10–13 cm (4–5 inches); you need 30 squares in total. Place one square on a board and spray with the cooking spray. Spray two more squares and stack them on top of the first square.

**3** Spread a small amount of Thai paste over the centre of the pastry and then top with about 1 tablespoon of the prawn mixture. Bring the sides of the pastry up and pinch together.

**4** Spray with a little cooking spray and place on a baking tray.

**5** Repeat with the remaining pastry and prawn mixture. Bake in the oven for 15 minutes until golden.

# Chilli crab and mango salad

**4** ProPoints value

Serves **4**

*ProPoints* values per recipe | **15** | calories per serving | **205**

This recipe is based on a South East Asian salad and is delicious.

*Preparation time 5 minutes*

240 g (8½ oz) fresh crabmeat or 2 x 120 g cans white crabmeat, drained

1 cucumber, grated

8 small pink radishes, halved and sliced thinly

2 ripe mangos or papayas, peeled, stoned or de-seeded and sliced

2 teaspoons caster sugar

1½ teaspoons fish or soy sauce

1 teaspoon dried crushed chilli

juice of 2 limes

salt

TO GARNISH

1 small red chilli, de-seeded and chopped

50 g (1¾ oz) roasted peanuts, chopped

a small bunch of fresh chives or coriander, chopped

**1** Put all the ingredients except the garnish in a bowl and toss together gently. Pile on to serving plates, then sprinkle with the chilli, peanuts and chives or coriander and serve.

# Chicken Kiev

**7** ProPoints value

Serves: **4**

| ProPoints values per recipe | 28 | calories per serving | 280 |

Serve with 100 g (3½ oz) low fat chips and zero *ProPoints* value vegetables such as fine green beans, cauliflower or carrots – or all three. Add 4 *ProPoints* values per serving.

*Preparation time 20 minutes l Cooking time 35–40 minutes*

low fat cooking spray
4 x 150 g (5½ oz) skinless boneless chicken breasts
125 g (4½ oz) low fat soft cheese with garlic and herbs
2 tablespoons plain white flour
1 egg, beaten with 2 tablespoons cold water
50 g (1¾ oz) fresh white breadcrumbs
salt and freshly ground black pepper

**1** Preheat the oven to Gas Mark 5/190°C/fan oven 170°C. Mist a baking dish or baking tray with the cooking spray.

**2** Put the chicken breasts, well spaced apart, between sheets of cling film or greaseproof paper. Use a meat mallet or rolling pin to beat them out until flattened, but avoid bashing them until they break up. Remove the cling film or paper.

**3** Divide the soft cheese into four equal portions. Place the cheese portions on the chicken breasts, towards the wider end of the chicken. Season. Roll up the breasts, folding in the sides to encase the cheese. Use cocktail sticks to secure them.

**4** Roll the chicken parcels in the flour and then dip them into the beaten egg mixture. Finally, roll them in the breadcrumbs and place in the dish or on the baking sheet.

**5** Bake for 35–40 minutes, until golden brown and thoroughly cooked. To check, pierce the chicken with a skewer or sharp knife – the juices should run clear. Remove the cocktail sticks before serving.

VARIATION For an extra garlic hit, spread ½ teaspoon of garlic purée over each chicken breast before adding the cheese. The *ProPoints* values will remain the same.

# Chicory and blue cheese tart

5 ProPoints value

Serves **4 V** ❄

| ProPoints values per recipe | 20 | calories per serving | 211 |

A lovely combination of flavours and textures that makes this an interesting dish. Serve with a big mixed zero *ProPoints* value salad.
*Preparation time 35 minutes  l Cooking 40–45 minutes*

15 g (½ oz) low fat spread
4 heads of chicory, sliced in half lengthways
450 g (1 lb) potatoes, peeled and cut into pieces
1 teaspoon English mustard
50 g (1¾ oz) blue cheese, crumbled
1 egg
150 ml (5 fl oz) skimmed milk
salt and freshly ground black pepper

**1** Preheat the oven to Gas Mark 7/220°C/fan oven 200°C. Melt the low fat spread in a lidded, non stick frying pan and gently fry the chicory, with a lid on, for 20 minutes, until softened.
**2** Meanwhile, bring a pan of water to the boil and cook the potatoes for about 20 minutes. Drain and mash with the mustard and seasoning.
**3** Line a 20 cm (8 inch) loose bottomed cake tin with non stick baking parchment, pile in the mash and press down to make a base. Bake in the oven for 15 minutes, until it has formed a crust.
**4** Arrange the braised chicory on top of the potato base and scatter with the blue cheese. In a jug, beat together the egg and milk with some seasoning. Pour over the chicory and return to the oven for a further 10–15 minutes, until the top is golden.

# Steak and chips with béarnaise sauce

15 ProPoints value

Serves **2** ❄

| ProPoints values per recipe | 31 | calories per serving | 704 |

*Preparation and cooking time 45 minutes*

700 g (1 lb 9 oz) potatoes, peeled and chopped into chips
low fat cooking spray
sea salt
2 x 105 g (3½ oz) lean beef fillet steaks

FOR THE BÉARNAISE SAUCE
3 tablespoons white wine vinegar
1 shallot, diced
6 black peppercorns
1 teaspoon dried tarragon
2 egg yolks
1 teaspoon Dijon mustard
150 g (5½ oz) low fat soft cheese
1 tablespoon chopped fresh tarragon

**1** Preheat the oven to Gas Mark 7/220°C/fan oven 200°C.
**2** Bring a pan of water to the boil and cook the potatoes until just tender. Drain on kitchen towel. Spray a baking tray with the cooking spray and then put the potatoes on it. Spray again and sprinkle with sea salt. Cook in the oven for 15 minutes. Turn them all, then cook for another 10–15 minutes until they are golden.
**3** Meanwhile, put the vinegar, shallot, peppercorns and dried tarragon into a small pan with 2 tablespoons of water. Bring to the boil and simmer until very little liquid is left. Strain and reserve.
**4** Put the egg yolks into a bowl over a pan of simmering water. Whisk in the mustard. Gently whisk in the vinegar liquid and finally the soft cheese, a little at a time. If at any stage the sauce starts to look grainy, just pour in a little boiling water and whisk furiously – it will come back together. Stir in the fresh tarragon. Keep warm.
**5** Grill the steak to your liking and serve with the chips and béarnaise sauce.

# Onion and rosemary tarte tatin

**7** *ProPoints value*

Serves **6 V**

| **ProPoints** values per recipe | **40** | calories per serving | **250** |

A really tasty tart – caramelised onions with a hint of rosemary on top of luscious, light puff pastry. Serve with a crisp, zero **ProPoints** value green salad.

*Preparation time 20–25 minutes  l Cooking  time 15 minutes*

low fat cooking spray
1 large onion, halved and sliced thickly
1 large red onion, halved and sliced thickly
2 garlic cloves, sliced
leaves from 3–4 fresh rosemary sprigs
350 g (12 oz) ready made puff pastry
salt and freshly ground black pepper

**1** Preheat the oven to Gas Mark 7/220°C/fan oven 200°C.
**2** Heat the cooking spray in a medium, lidded, non stick pan and add the onions and garlic. When they start to cook, turn the heat down to very low and cover the pan. Cook for 15–20 minutes, stirring occasionally, until they start to caramelise. Season well.
**3** Add the rosemary to the pan and stir in. Pour the onion mixture into a 23 cm (9 inch) flan tin.
**4** Roll out the pastry and cut to fit the tin. Place on top of the onions and tuck in the edges.
**5** Bake for 12–15 minutes until the top is golden.
**6** Turn out on to a plate so the onions are on top. Serve warm.

# Chocolate mocha mousse

**4** *ProPoints value*

Serves **4 V**

| **ProPoints** values per recipe | **17** | calories per serving | **147** |

These rich, fluffy mousses look great in espresso cups with crème fraîche and a pinch of cocoa powder.

*Preparation time 30 minutes + minimum 30 minutes chilling*

50 g (1¾ oz) plain cooking chocolate (preferably 70% cocoa solids), broken into pieces
1 tablespoon instant coffee, dissolved in 2 tablespoons boiling water, or 2 tablespoons very strong real coffee
4 teaspoons golden syrup
2 egg whites
140 g (5 oz) low fat soft cheese, at room temperature
4 teaspoons half fat crème fraîche, to serve
1 teaspoon cocoa powder, to serve

**1** Place the chocolate in a large heatproof bowl with the coffee and golden syrup. Set over a small saucepan of simmering water until the chocolate melts. Stir together and remove from the heat. Allow to cool slightly – about 10 minutes – until warm but not hot.
**2** In a separate bowl, whisk the egg whites until stiff.
**3** Whisk the soft cheese and melted chocolate together until smooth. Gently fold in the egg whites.
**4** Spoon into four serving glasses, espresso cups or pots and refrigerate for at least 30 minutes, until chilled and set. Decorate each mousse with a teaspoon of crème fraîche and a dusting of cocoa powder to serve.

**TOP TIP** To whisk egg whites, use eggs that have been left at room temperature and a large mixing bowl that is clean and dry. Separate the eggs and put the whites in the bowl, making sure they are completely free of yolk. Use a whisk (either hand held or electric) and beat until the egg whites are stiff and form peaks when lifted.

# Strawberry syllabub 3 ProPoints value

Serves **2**  V ❋ *(see tip)*

| **ProPoints** values per recipe | 6 | calories per serving | 80 |

In the summer months, when fresh strawberries are in abundance, make the most of them as they are both delicious and low in **ProPoints** values.

*Preparation and cooking time 15 minutes + 30 minutes chilling*

175 g (6 oz) fresh strawberries, hulled and sliced
1 tablespoon artificial sweetener
1 tablespoon port
175 ml (6 fl oz) low fat strawberry fromage frais

**1** Reserve 1 strawberry and place the rest in a food processor with the sweetener and port. Blend until smooth.

**2** Place the fromage frais in a mixing bowl and stir in the strawberry purée.

**3** Divide the syllabub mixture between two small dishes and chill for 30 minutes. Decorate each one with slices of the reserved strawberry before serving.

TOP TIP  You can freeze this mixture to make a superb ice cream. Take it out of the freezer 20 minutes before serving.

# Red cherry and ginger slice

Serves **8**

| **ProPoints** values per recipe | 44 | calories per serving | 200 |

Member Janet Smith from Scarborough in North Yorkshire has devised this indulgent dessert to keep sweet cravings at bay. It uses low fat ingredients to keep the **ProPoints** values in check, though you'd never guess it was a Weight Watchers pudding.

*Preparation time 25 minutes + several hours chilling*

50 g (1¾ oz) low fat spread
150 g (5½ oz) Rich Tea or Morning Coffee biscuits
½ teaspoon ground ginger
4 tablespoons boiling water
12 g sachet powdered gelatine
397 g can cherry pie filling
4 teaspoons artificial sweetener
500 g carton virtually fat free fromage frais
25 g (1 oz) crystallised ginger, chopped finely, to decorate

1 Line an 18 cm (7 inch) loose based cake tin with cling film.
2 Melt the low fat spread and stir in the crushed biscuits and ground ginger. Tip them into the prepared tin and press down evenly over the base. Chill in the refrigerator.
3 Put 4 tablespoons of just boiled water into a bowl and sprinkle in the gelatine. Stir to disperse, then allow 4–5 minutes for it to dissolve into a completely clear liquid.
4 Tip the cherry pie filling into a mixing bowl and add the gelatine liquid, stirring thoroughly. Add the sweetener, then fold in the fromage frais. Pour this mixture over the biscuit base and spread out evenly. Cover and chill for several hours, or overnight, to set.
5 Just before serving, carefully lift from the tin and remove the cling film. Cut into eight portions and decorate with finely chopped crystallised ginger.

VARIATIONS Try a different pie filling, such as blackcurrant or raspberry. Use stem ginger in syrup, well rinsed, instead of the crystallised ginger.

# White chocolate dreamcake

6 ProPoints value

Serves **8** ❄

| **ProPoints** values per recipe | **47** | calories per serving | **205** |

A sumptuously creamy, beautiful pink mousse.
*Preparation and cooking time 20 minutes + chilling time + 2 hours setting*

100 g (3½ oz) reduced fat digestive biscuits
50 g (1¾ oz) low fat spread, melted

**FOR THE TOPPING**
100 g (3½ oz) white chocolate, broken into pieces
400 ml (14 fl oz) low fat natural yogurt
11 g sachet powdered gelatine
6 tablespoons boiling water
300 g can raspberries in syrup

**TO GARNISH (OPTIONAL)**
a few fresh raspberries
fresh mint leaves

**1** Pulverise the biscuits in a food processor, add the melted low fat spread then press into a 20 cm (8 inch) loose bottomed flan tin and chill.

**2** Melt the chocolate in a bowl set over a pan of simmering water. Put the yogurt in a bowl and stir in the chocolate. Sprinkle the gelatine over the boiling water in a small pan then heat gently and stir until dissolved. Cool a little and then stir into the yogurt mixture.

**3** Drain 6 tablespoons of the syrup from the raspberries and discard, then add the rest of the syrup along with the berries to the yogurt mixture. Pour into the biscuit base and chill for at least 2 hours until set.

**4** Serve decorated with whole raspberries and mint leaves, if using.

# Chocolate Victoria sponge

(4) ProPoints value

Makes **8** slices ✳ *sponges only*

| **ProPoints** values per recipe | 30 | calories per serving | 145 |

There is something very appealing about a chocolate cake, and this fat free sponge isn't as naughty as it looks.

*Preparation time 25 minutes l Baking time 20 minutes*

3 eggs
75 g (2¾ oz) caster sugar
75 g (2¾ oz) plain white flour
25 g (1 oz) cocoa powder

**FOR THE FILLING**
3 tablespoons reduced sugar strawberry jam
100 ml (3½ fl oz) 0% fat Greek yogurt

**TO DECORATE**
1 teaspoon icing sugar
15 g (½ oz) plain chocolate curls

**1** Preheat the oven to Gas Mark 4/180°C/fan oven 160°C. Line the base of two 19 cm (7½ inch) round, non stick cake tins with non stick baking parchment.

**2** Place the eggs and caster sugar in a mixing bowl and whisk with electric beaters for 5 minutes, until you have a pale, fluffy mixture – when you lift the whisk, it should leave a trail.

**3** Sift in the flour and cocoa powder and fold them in using a metal spoon, taking care not to knock too much air out. Divide the mixture between the two tins and bake for 20 minutes until the sponges are firm and springy to the touch. Transfer the cakes to a wire rack to cool completely.

**4** When cool, spread one of the cakes with the jam, top with the yogurt and place the second cake over the top. Put the cake on a serving plate and dust the top with icing sugar, then scatter the chocolate curls over the top.

**VARIATION**  Real chocolate lovers can use low fat chocolate yogurt for the filling instead of Greek yogurt. The **ProPoints** values per serving will remain the same.

# Time to bake

# Quick and easy wholemeal bread

**3** ProPoints value

*Makes **2** medium loaves which cut into about 16 slices each* **V** ❄

| **ProPoints** values per recipe | 83 | calories per slice | 95 |

Home made bread has many advantages over its shop bought equivalents, including being less expensive and containing fewer additives. It is tasty, satisfying and, most importantly, you know exactly how many *ProPoints* values are in it. This bread is delicious served with any of the scrumptious soups in this book or toasted and spread with reduced sugar jam or marmalade for an extra 1 *ProPoints* value per heaped teaspoon.

*Preparation time 15 minutes + 45 minutes–1 hour rising l Cooking time 35–40 minutes*

900 g (2 lb) plain wholemeal flour, plus extra for dusting

10 g (¼ oz) salt

15 g (½ oz) soft brown sugar

15 g (½ oz) fresh yeast or 10 g (¼ oz) dried yeast

600 ml (20 fl oz) warm water

low fat cooking spray

1  Mix the flour, salt and sugar together in a large bowl. Make a well in the centre.

2  Mix the yeast into a wet paste with a little warm water and pour into the well with a little more of the water.

3  Mix together with your hands, adding more water if it is too dry, until you have a slippery dough that comes away from the bowl in a smooth ball. Different flours vary in their absorbency so add the water a bit at a time in case the dough becomes too wet and sticky.

4  Divide the dough between two 13 x 23 cm (5 x 9 inch) bread tins that have been warmed and sprayed with the cooking spray. Cover with a clean, floured tea towel and leave in a warm place until the dough has risen by more than a half, usually around 45 minutes–1 hour.

5  Preheat the oven to Gas Mark 6/200°C/fan oven 180°C. Sprinkle the loaves with flour and bake for 35–40 minutes. Check that they are cooked by tapping the bottom – they should sound hollow.

TOP TIPS  This recipe makes two medium loaves – one to eat and one to wrap in a plastic bag and freeze for up to 3 months. Uncooked bread will rise if you leave it in the fridge but it will take 24 hours, so it is not absolutely necessary to put it in a warm place but it does speed up the process. If you put it in an airing cupboard, on top of the boiler or on top of the oven, then the dough will rise quickly giving a more open texture than if left in the kitchen for, say, 1½ hours, when it rises very gently.

VARIATIONS  Your bread will vary greatly depending on the flour that you use, so try different brands and types or try mixing types, for example use half white and half wholemeal flour, or half white and half rye flour. Organic and stoneground flours are well worth a try as most give a lovely texture and flavour. Always use a 'strong' bread flour, as this means that it has a high gluten content that will make it rise better.

# Tomato bread

6 ProPoints value

Serves **6 V** ❄

| **ProPoints** values per recipe | 34 | calories per serving | 189 |

This recipe contains no yeast so there's no waiting. It makes a delicious savoury bread that's ideal with soup or stews.

*Preparation time 25 minutes l Cooking time 15 minutes*

225 g (8 oz) plain flour, plus extra for dusting

a pinch of salt

3 teaspoons baking powder

25 g (1 oz) sun-dried tomatoes, soaked for 10 minutes in boiling water, then drained and chopped

4 spring onions, chopped finely

200 ml (7 fl oz) skimmed milk

2 tablespoons olive oil

freshly ground black pepper

1 Preheat the oven to Gas Mark 7/220°C/fan oven 200°C. Sift the flour, salt and baking powder into a large bowl. Grind in a little black pepper and stir in the chopped sun-dried tomatoes and spring onions.

2 Mix 150 ml (5 fl oz) of the milk and the oil together and add to the flour mixture. Gently combine to make a soft and manageable dough, adding the extra milk if necessary.

3 On a lightly floured surface, roll out the dough to about 2.5 cm (1 inch) thick. Form into a round about 15 cm (6 inches) in diameter. Score into six triangles with a knife, taking care not to cut all the way through the dough.

4 Place on a baking tray lined with non stick baking parchment and bake for 12–15 minutes, until the bread is risen and golden.

# Garlic and coriander naan bread

ProPoints value 6

Makes **8 V** ❄

| **ProPoints** values per recipe | 45 | calories per serving | 190 |

These puffy naan breads are an ideal accompaniment to a lovely saucy curry instead of rice, or they can be split open and filled as an alternative to a sandwich.

*Preparation time 15 minutes + 1½ hours rising l Cooking time 5 minutes*

400 g (14 oz) plain flour, plus 1 tablespoon for kneading and
   1 tablespoon for rolling
1 teaspoon fast action yeast
1 teaspoon salt
150 ml (5 fl oz) low fat natural yogurt
2 garlic cloves, crushed
3 tablespoons chopped fresh coriander

1 Mix the flour with the yeast and salt in a large bowl. Make a well in the centre and pour in the yogurt, then add up to 125 ml (4 fl oz) of warm water to bring together as a soft dough. Turn out on to a lightly floured surface and knead for 3 minutes until soft and springy. Stretch out the dough and scatter with the garlic and coriander. Knead again until evenly distributed throughout the dough.

2 Return the dough to the bowl and cover with cling film. Leave to rise in a warm place for 1½ hours or until doubled in bulk.

3 Preheat the oven to Gas Mark 8/230°C/fan oven 210°C. Place two large baking trays in the oven to preheat.

4 Divide the dough into eight pieces. Roll each one out on a lightly floured surface to an oval shape measuring about 12 x 18 cm (4½ x 7 inches). Bake the naan bread on the preheated baking trays for 5 minutes, or until puffy and browned in patches. Serve warm.

TOP TIP To freeze the naan breads, wrap them individually in cling film once cooled, then freeze in a plastic bag for up to 1 month.

# Fruit scones

**4** ProPoints value

Serves **8 V** ☀

| **ProPoints** values per recipe | 34 | calories per serving | 185 |

For a special treat, serve each scone with a teaspoon of reduced sugar strawberry jam and a tablespoon of low fat aerosol cream. This will add 1 **ProPoints** value per serving.

*Preparation and cooking time 20 minutes*

low fat cooking spray
225 g (8 oz) self raising white flour, plus extra for rolling
a pinch of salt
50 g (1¾ oz) low fat spread
25 g (1 oz) golden caster sugar
50 g (1¾ oz) sultanas or raisins
1 egg
4 tablespoons skimmed milk

**1** Preheat the oven to Gas Mark 7/220°C/fan oven 200°C. Mist a baking tray with the cooking spray.

**2** Sift the flour and salt into a large mixing bowl. Add the low fat spread and rub it in with your fingertips until the mixture resembles fine breadcrumbs. Stir in the sugar and sultanas or raisins.

**3** Beat the egg and milk together and add just enough to the rubbed in mixture to give a soft, but not sticky, dough. Knead lightly for a few moments, but avoid over handling it.

**4** On a lightly floured surface roll out the dough so that it is about 2 cm (¾ inch) thick – it's a mistake to roll it out too thinly. Cut into eight rounds using a 5 cm (2 inch) cutter, re-rolling the dough if necessary. Place these rounds on the baking tray and brush the tops with the remaining egg and milk mixture.

**5** Bake for 10–12 minutes until risen and golden brown. Cool on a wire rack for about 10–15 minutes. These scones are at their best when served while still warm.

VARIATION Use chopped ready to eat dried apricots or dates instead of the sultanas or raisins. The **ProPoints** values will remain the same.

# Carrot cake with orange icing

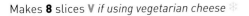

Makes **8** slices **V** *if using vegetarian cheese* ❄

| **ProPoints** values per recipe | 33 | calories per slice | 190 |
|---|---|---|---|

Carrot cake with its moist texture and natural sweetness is always popular. This version has a zesty orange icing to really get the tastebuds tingling.

*Preparation time 15 minutes + cooling l Cooking time 20 minutes*

low fat cooking spray

2 eggs

100 g (3½ oz) caster sugar

50 g (1¾ oz) low fat spread, melted

175 g (6 oz) carrots, peeled and grated

100 g (3½ oz) self raising flour, sifted

1 teaspoon ground cinnamon

½ teaspoon ground nutmeg

FOR THE ORANGE ICING

50 g (1¾ oz) low fat soft cheese

25 g (1 oz) icing sugar

zest of an orange and 1 tablespoon of the juice

**1** Preheat the oven to Gas Mark 5/190°C/fan oven 170°C. Spray an 18 cm (7 inch) round cake tin with the cooking spray, line the base with baking parchment then spray again.

**2** Whisk the eggs and sugar together until light and fluffy. Gradually whisk in the melted low fat spread then add all the remaining cake ingredients.

**3** Pour into the tin and bake for 20 minutes or until golden brown and firm to the touch. Turn out of the tin and leave on a wire rack to cool.

**4** Make the icing by beating together the soft cheese, sugar, orange zest and juice then spread over the cooled cake.

TOP TIP Carrot cake will keep for several days in an airtight container.

# Oatmeal biscuits

$\boxed{2}$ ProPoints value

Makes **12** biscuits **V** ❄

| **ProPoints** values per recipe | 20 | calories per serving | 70 |

Make a batch of these delicious, crunchy biscuits and freeze them, then just remove one when you want a snack, allowing a little defrosting time.

*Preparation time 10 minutes l Cooking time 15 minutes*

50 g (1¾ oz) plain white flour, plus 2 teaspoons for rolling
a good pinch of bicarbonate of soda
100 g (3½ oz) oatmeal
2 teaspoons light soft brown sugar (optional)
25 g (1 oz) raisins (optional)
25 g (1 oz) low fat spread
5 tablespoons hot water

1 Heat the oven to Gas Mark 7/220°C/fan oven 200°C. Sift together the flour, bicarbonate of soda, oatmeal and sugar, if using. Stir in the raisins, if using.

2 Mix together the low fat spread and hot water, stirring until the low fat spread has melted. Beat this mixture into the dry ingredients to make a firm, but not dry, dough. If necessary, add extra dribbles of hot water.

3 Turn out the dough on to a wooden board dusted with a little flour. Roll out to 5 mm (¼ inch) thickness. Cut the dough into neat squares, measuring about 5 cm (2 inches).

4 Line a heavy baking tray with non stick baking parchment and place the oatmeal biscuits on top. Prick each one two or three times with a fork. Bake in the oven for 15 minutes until firm, then transfer to a wire tray to cool completely.

TOP TIP You need old fashioned oatmeal for these biscuits to give them a lovely crisp texture. Most supermarkets stock it these days, or try the health food shops.

# Fruit and nut bites

$\boxed{2}$ ProPoints value

Makes **20** slices **V**

| **ProPoints** values per recipe | 37 | calories per slice | 60 |

Anne Wilkinson, a Member from Harrogate in North Yorkshire, is a retired Health Visitor. She developed this recipe from one originally created for her children as a healthier alternative to real sweets.

*Preparation time 10 minutes + 2 hours standing time*

50 g (1¾ oz) dried mango slices
100 g (3½ oz) blanched almonds
75 g (2¾ oz) raisins
175 g (6 oz) ready to eat dried apricots
1 tablespoon cocoa powder
1 tablespoon cold tea
approximately 4 sheets of rice paper

1 In a blender or food processor, blend together the mango slices, almonds, raisins, apricots, cocoa powder and cold tea.

2 Divide the mixture into two and place between sheets of rice paper, levelling the mixture out by hand, then flattening and spreading out with a rolling pin, so that the mixture is about 5 mm (¼ inch) thick.

3 Leave for about 2 hours, then cut into pieces with a sharp knife or scissors to make 20 bites.

4 Store in an airtight container.

TOP TIP Rice paper can be bought from supermarkets and good kitchenware suppliers. It is edible.

# No-fat bara brith

⌂ 5 ProPoints value ®

Serves **14 V** ❄

| **ProPoints** values per recipe | 74 | calories per slice | 200 |

Christine Parkman, from Barry in South Glamorgan, has developed a delicious low fat version of a Welsh family favourite, bara brith, a moist dark fruit cake. Since becoming a Member, Christine has improved her health and fitness and feels much better for it.

*Preparation time 10 minutes + overnight standing l Cooking time 1¼–1½ hours*

250 g (9 oz) dark muscovado sugar
250 g (9 oz) mixed dried fruit
250 ml (9 fl oz) cold tea
low fat cooking spray
300 g (10½ oz) self raising flour
1 egg, beaten

**1** Put the sugar and dried fruit into a large mixing bowl and cover with the cold tea. Stir well, then cover and allow to stand overnight.

**2** Next day, preheat the oven to Gas Mark 4/180°C/fan oven 160°C. Grease a 1 kg (2 lb 4 oz) loaf tin with the cooking spray and line with non stick baking parchment.

**3** Gradually add the flour and egg to the soaked fruit mixture. When thoroughly mixed, transfer to the prepared tin and bake for 1¼ hours. To test that the cake is cooked, insert a skewer into the centre of the cake – it should come out clean. If not, return to the oven for another few minutes.

**4** Cool in the tin on a wire rack and, when completely cold, turn out, wrap in foil and keep for 2–3 days before cutting.

TOP TIP The cake is moist enough to eat alone but, if you wish, spread it with 1 teaspoon of low fat spread, for a further 1 **ProPoints** value per slice.

# Italian chocolate cake

⌂ 5 ProPoints value ®

Serves **8**

| **ProPoints** values per recipe | 41 | calories per serving | 230 |

This is a fantastically chocolately cake, and the semolina adds a lovely nutty crunch.

*Preparation time 15 minutes l Cooking time 35 minutes*

low fat cooking spray
110 g (4 oz) low fat spread
110 g (4 oz) caster sugar
2 eggs, separated
25 g (1 oz) self raising flour
60 g (2 oz) cocoa powder, 1 teaspoon reserved for dusting
60 g (2 oz) dried semolina
4 tablespoons skimmed milk

**1** Preheat the oven to Gas Mark 4/180°C/fan oven 160°C. Spray a 20 cm (8 inch) spring form cake tin with the cooking spray and line the base with non stick baking parchment.

**2** Using an electric whisk, cream the low fat spread and sugar together until pale and smooth – you should notice a change in the colour. Beat the egg yolks together and gradually whisk in, beating between additions until combined.

**3** Sift the flour and cocoa powder into the bowl, then add the semolina and the milk. Use a large metal spoon to carefully fold in until combined.

**4** Whisk the egg whites until they hold stiff peaks. Add a spoonful to the cake mixture and fold in to slacken it, then carefully fold in the remaining egg white.

**5** Pour the mixture into the prepared tin and bake for 30–35 minutes until firm to the touch. Cool in the tin.

**6** Remove the cake from the tin, dust with the reserved cocoa powder and serve in slices.

# Banana cake

Serves **10 V** ❄ *cake for up to 1 month (the filling cannot be frozen)*

| ***ProPoints*** values per recipe | 34 | calories per serving | 168 |

*Preparation time  25 minutes l Baking time 30 minutes + cooling*

200 g (7 oz) dried polenta
150 g (5½ oz) low fat soft cheese
4 tablespoons artificial sweetener
3 eggs, separated
2 soft bananas, mashed with a fork
½ teaspoon baking powder
low fat cooking spray

FOR THE FILLING
150 g (5½ oz) low fat soft cheese
1½ teaspoons artificial sweetener
grated zest of an orange
1 banana
juice of ½ a lemon

1 Cook the polenta according to the packet instructions and set aside. Preheat the oven to Gas Mark 4/180°C/fan oven 160°C.

2 Cream together the low fat soft cheese and sweetener, then whisk in the egg yolks and mashed banana.

3 Fold in the polenta and baking powder. Whisk the egg whites in a separate bowl until stiff. Fold them into the polenta mixture.

4 Spray two 18 cm (7 inch) tins with the cooking spray and line the bases with non stick baking parchment. Divide the mixture between the two tins and bake for 30 minutes or until firm to the touch.

5 Allow the cakes to rest for 5 minutes and then remove from the tins. Leave to cool on a cooling rack.

6 For the filling, cream together the soft cheese, sweetener and orange zest and spread over one of the cakes.

7 Slice the banana and toss in the lemon juice before placing on top of the creamy filling. Place the other cake on top and serve.

# Luscious lemon fairy cakes

3 ProPoints value

Makes **9** cakes **V**

| **ProPoints** values per recipe | 23 | calories per serving | 105 |

The fresh, zesty flavour of lemons make these little cakes a popular treat.

*Preparation time 10 minutes l Baking time 15 minutes*

75 g (2¾ oz) self raising white flour
50 g (1¾ oz) low fat spread
50 g (1¾ oz) caster sugar
1 egg, beaten
finely grated zest of a lemon
1 tablespoon fresh lemon juice

FOR THE TOPPING
1 tablespoon lemon curd
1 tablespoon boiling water

1  Preheat the oven to Gas Mark 5/190°C/fan oven 170°C. Line a nine hole bun tin with paper cases.

2  Sift the flour into a bowl. In a separate mixing bowl, beat the low fat spread and sugar together until you have a pale and fluffy mixture. Add the beaten egg, lemon zest and lemon juice with 1 tablespoon of the flour and mix well.

3  Add the remaining flour to the lemon mixture and fold it in thoroughly. Divide the mixture between the paper cases and bake for 15 minutes, until the sponges are springy to the touch.

4  While the cakes are still warm, mix the lemon curd with the boiling water and brush this over the surface of the cakes. Allow them to cool before serving.

# Black Forest gâteau

6 ProPoints value

Serves **8** **V** *if using vegetarian fromage frais* ❋

| **ProPoints** values per recipe | 48 | calories per serving | 240 |

A low fat version of this classic chocolate cake.
*Preparation time 20 minutes + approximately 1 hour cooling time l Cooking time 25 minutes*

1 tablespoon cocoa powder, for dusting

FOR THE CHOCOLATE CAKE
low fat cooking spray
100 g (3½ oz) low fat spread
50 g (1¾ oz) soft brown sugar
1 teaspoon vanilla essence
25 g (1 oz) low fat drinking chocolate
2 eggs
100 g (3½ oz) self raising flour

FOR THE FILLING
1 tablespoon icing sugar
200 g (7 oz) virtually fat free fromage frais
425 g can stoned cherries in syrup, drained with 2 tablespoons
    syrup reserved and cut in half
2 tablespoons kirsch (optional)

1  Preheat the oven to Gas Mark 4/180°C/fan oven 160°C and spray an 18 cm (7 inch) cake tin with the cooking spray.
2  Cream together the low fat spread and sugar then add the vanilla essence and drinking chocolate and then the eggs, one at a time, and beat well together. Sieve in the flour, fold into the mixture and spoon into the prepared tin. Bake for 25 minutes or until springy to the touch and a skewer inserted into the centre comes out clean.
3  Turn the cake out on to a cooling rack and allow to cool completely (about 1 hour), then slice in half to make 2 thinner cakes.
4  For the filling, stir the icing sugar into the fromage frais. Spoon 2 tablespoons of the juice from the cherries over one of the sponges with the kirsch, if using.
5  Thickly spread the fromage frais over the sponge and top with the drained cherries. Put the other sponge cake on top and gently press down. Dust the top with cocoa powder and serve, or chill then serve.

# Rich dark fruit cake

Makes **20** slices **V** ❄

| **ProPoints** values per recipe | 151 | calories per slice | 275 |

We all have a favourite rich fruit cake recipe. But at times when we want to have that special celebration cake without the high fat content, isn't it great to have an alternative recipe that means you can stick to tradition without it sticking to the hips.

*Preparation time 25 minutes l Cooking time 1¾ hours*

350 g (12 oz) ready to eat prunes
6 tablespoons brandy or sherry
finely grated zest and juice of a large lemon
finely grated zest and juice of a large orange
200 g (7 oz) dark muscovado sugar
4 eggs
1 tablespoon black treacle
1 cooking apple, peeled, cored and grated
350 g (12 oz) plain flour
2 teaspoons baking powder
2 teaspoons mixed spice
½ teaspoon ground nutmeg
800 g (1 lb 11 oz) luxury dried mixed fruits
6 tablespoons semi skimmed milk

1 Heat the oven to Gas Mark 4/180°C/fan oven 160°C. Line a deep 23 cm (9 inch) round cake tin with baking parchment.
2 Purée the prunes in a food processor or liquidiser, together with the brandy or sherry, lemon and orange zest and juice. Transfer to a bowl and whisk in the sugar and eggs until the mixture becomes light and fluffy. Whisk in the treacle.
3 Use a metal spoon to stir in the apple, flour, baking powder and spices. Finally mix in the dried fruit and enough milk to form a soft dropping consistency. Transfer to the prepared tin, levelling out the surface.

4 Bake in the centre of the oven for 45 minutes, then reduce the oven temperature to Gas Mark 3/160°C/fan oven 140°C and continue to cook for 1 hour or until the cake is well risen and a skewer inserted in the centre comes out clean.
5 Leave the cake to cool in the tin before removing and discarding the baking parchment. Wrap the cake in fresh paper or foil and store in an airtight tin. The cake is best left for at least a day to mature before cutting.

TOP TIP An old wives' tale or not, I always leave a whole apple in the storage container alongside my fruit cakes to help keep them moist.

VARIATION To decorate the cake, brush the surface with 1 tablespoon of apricot jam and roll out 175 g (6 oz) of ready prepared icing. Press firmly on to the cake, trim the edges and decorate with strips of lemon or orange rind. This will add 1 **ProPoints** value per slice.

# Apple and cinnamon ring

Makes **10** slices **V**

| **ProPoints** values per recipe | 42 | calories per slice | 170 |

*Preparation time 20 minutes l Baking time 40 minutes*

low fat cooking spray

350 g (12 oz) cooking apples, peeled, cored and grated coarsely

2 tablespoons lemon juice

150 g (5½ oz) self raising white flour

1 teaspoon baking powder

½ teaspoon ground cinnamon

50 g (1¾ oz) demerara sugar

50 g (1¾ oz) sultanas

50 ml (2 fl oz) sunflower oil

2 eggs

100 ml (3½ fl oz) skimmed milk

2 tablespoons reduced sugar apricot jam

**1** Preheat the oven to Gas Mark 4/180°C/fan oven 160°C. Spray an 850 ml (1½ pint) ring mould with a little cooking spray. Mix the grated apples with the lemon juice.

**2** Sift the flour, baking powder and cinnamon into a mixing bowl. Stir in the grated apple mixture, sugar and sultanas. Make a well in the centre of the mixture.

**3** Beat together the oil, eggs, milk and jam. Pour this into the well in the dry ingredients and mix everything together.

**4** Spoon the mixture into the prepared mould and level the surface with the back of a spoon. Bake for 35–40 minutes, or until the cake is browned, firm and springy to the touch. Cool in the tin for 10 minutes then loosen the edges with a palette knife and turn it out on to a cooling rack.

TOP TIP Before serving, dust with ½ teaspoon of icing sugar, if desired. This will not alter the **ProPoints** values.

# Sticky cranberry gammon

8 ProPoints value

Serves **1**

| **ProPoints** values per recipe | 8 | calories per serving | 367 |

*Preparation and cooking time 30 minutes*

150 g (5½ oz) lean gammon steak, visible fat removed
1 teaspoon honey
50 g (1¾ oz) frozen or fresh cranberries
2 teaspoons wholegrain mustard
50 g (1¾ oz) mange tout or sugarsnap peas
50 g (1¾ oz) green beans
50 g (1¾ oz) peas
salt and freshly ground black pepper

1 Preheat the grill to high and lay the gammon steak on the grill pan. In a small, covered saucepan, heat the honey with the cranberries, 1 teaspoon of the mustard, seasoning and 2 tablespoons of water. Cook for about 3–4 minutes, until the cranberries start to pop.
2 Brush the gammon steak with the cranberry mixture and grill for 5–6 minutes on each side, brushing frequently with the cranberry mixture.
3 Meanwhile, bring a pan of water to the boil and blanch the vegetables for 30 seconds, then toss with the remaining teaspoon of mustard and seasoning.
4 Serve the gammon with the vegetables and any remaining sauce poured over.

# Italian trifle

6 ProPoints value

Serves **4** V

| **ProPoints** values per recipe | 23 | calories per serving | 270 |

This velvety smooth Italian dessert is absolutely delicious.
*Preparation time 5 minutes + 30 minutes chilling*

4 trifle sponges
250 g (9 oz) ricotta
100 g (3½ oz) low fat soft cheese
2 tablespoons reduced sugar jam with extra fruit
450 g (1 lb) fresh or frozen mixed strawberries, raspberries and blueberries
400 g can peach slices in natural juice, drained and juice reserved
2 drops vanilla essence
fresh mint leaves, to decorate

1 Line the bottom of a large glass trifle bowl or four individual bowls with the trifle sponges.
2 In a separate bowl, beat together the ricotta, low fat soft cheese and jam.
3 Quarter the strawberries, if using fresh ones. Reserving a few berries for decoration, mix with the other berries, peach slices and juice and vanilla essence in a bowl. Spoon this mixture over the sponges.
4 Spread the cheese mixture evenly over the fruit and decorate with more berries and mint leaves. Refrigerate for at least 30 minutes before serving.

A festive feast

# Butterbean and broccoli soup

ProPoints value 4

Serves **4** ❄

| **ProPoints** values per recipe | **14** | calories per serving | **160** |

This is a truly satisfying soup – filling, tasty and packed full of nourishment to help keep the winter bugs at bay. Serve a generous bowlful with a medium slice of fresh crusty brown bread per person, for an extra 2 **ProPoints** values per serving. Great for the thermos flask too.

*Preparation time 15 minutes l Cooking time 20 minutes*

low fat cooking spray
2 x 25 g (1 oz) rashers rindless smoked lean back bacon, chopped
1 large onion, chopped
1 garlic clove, crushed
400 g (14 oz) broccoli, chopped roughly
1.2 litres (2 pints) hot chicken or vegetable stock
2 x 420 g cans butterbeans, rinsed and drained
1 teaspoon dried rosemary (or 1 tablespoon chopped fresh)
salt and freshly ground black pepper

1 Spray a large, lidded, non stick saucepan with the cooking spray and fry the bacon over a high heat until it is very crispy. Use a slotted spoon to transfer the bacon to a plate lined with kitchen towel. Set to one side.

2 Turn the heat down, add the onion, garlic and broccoli, cover and cook for 4–5 minutes or until softened, shaking the pan occasionally.

3 Pour in the stock and bring to the boil. Add the butterbeans, rosemary and seasoning to taste, then cover and simmer for 15 minutes until the broccoli is tender.

4 Liquidise two-thirds of the soup until smooth. Add the remaining third and liquidise for a short burst to coarsely chop the remaining vegetables. Return to the pan and reheat. Check the seasoning.

5 Ladle the soup into four warmed bowls and scatter on the crispy bacon bits. Serve immediately.

TOP TIP Choose broccoli that has good dark green florets – an indication of freshness and therefore higher nutritional value.

VEGETARIAN OPTION To make this soup suitable for vegetarians, replace the chicken stock with vegetable stock and omit the bacon rashers. You will save 1 **ProPoints** value per serving. For a special garnish, sprinkle 1 teaspoon of toasted flaked almonds over the soup. This will add 1 **ProPoints** value per serving.

# Roast Christmas turkey

10
ProPoints
value

Serves **6**

*ProPoints* values per recipe | **58** | calories per serving | **325**

*Preparation time 40 minutes l Cooking time 2 hours*

2.25 kg (5 lb) turkey
50 g (1¾ oz) streaky bacon rashers
salt and freshly ground black pepper

**FOR THE STUFFING**
low fat cooking spray
4 shallots, chopped finely
225 g (8 oz) mushrooms, chopped finely
125 g (4½ oz) fresh wholemeal breadcrumbs
2 teaspoons dried tarragon
2 tablespoons reduced sugar marmalade
3 tablespoons fresh orange juice

**FOR THE GRAVY**
300 ml (10 fl oz) chicken stock
2 tablespoons cornflour
2 tablespoons port

1 Rinse the turkey well and pat it dry thoroughly with kitchen towel. Place it in a large roasting tin.

2 Preheat the oven to Gas Mark 5/190°C/fan oven 170°C.

3 To make the stuffing, spray a medium, lidded saucepan with the cooking spray and add the shallots. Cook them gently until softened and then add the mushrooms. Cover and cook gently for 5 minutes until the mushrooms are tender. Remove the pan from the heat and mix in the breadcrumbs, tarragon, marmalade and orange juice. Fill the neck cavity of the turkey with the stuffing and then pull the neck flap of skin over the stuffing and tuck it under the bird, securing it with a cocktail stick. Season the turkey well and lay the bacon rashers over the breast in a criss-cross pattern.

4 Roast the turkey for 2 hours. When cooked, carefully lift it out of the roasting tin on to a large serving platter. Allow it to rest for 10 minutes before carving.

5 For the gravy, pour the turkey juices into a pan – skim off the fat first. Stir in the stock and bring it to the boil. Mix the cornflour with the port and stir this in. Cook, stirring, until the gravy thickens.

6 Thinly carve the turkey and serve 150 g (5½ oz) of meat per person with 50 g (1¾ oz) of the stuffing, your chosen zero *ProPoints* value vegetables and the gravy.

# Perfect roast potatoes

Serves **4 V**

| **ProPoints** values per recipe | **34** | calories per serving | **290** |

Always popular, but these have fewer *ProPoints* values than traditional roast potatoes – and they taste just as good.

*Preparation time 20 minutes l Cooking time 1 hour*

1 kg (2 1b 4 oz) peeled potatoes, each cut into three even sized
   pieces
8 teaspoons olive oil
1 tablespoon plain flour
low fat cooking spray
salt and freshly ground black pepper

1 Bring a pan of water to the boil and cook the potatoes for 10 minutes.
2 Preheat the oven to Gas Mark 7/220°C/fan oven 200°C and heat a large baking tray with the olive oil in it.
3 Drain the potatoes and return them to the saucepan. Cover with a lid and shake them about to soften their edges a bit, then sprinkle over the flour, replace the lid and shake again to part-coat.
4 Carefully remove the hot baking tray from the oven and transfer the potatoes on to it. Season well and turn the potatoes to coat them in oil. Spray with the cooking spray and roast for 30 minutes.
5 Remove from the oven, turn the potatoes, spray again and return to the oven for another 30 minutes, after which they should be golden brown and crispy on the outside, but soft in the middle.

# Spicy turkey cakes

Serves **4**

| **ProPoints** values per recipe | **19** | calories per serving | **150** |

These little cakes are good as an appetiser with drinks. Serve with a fresh tomato, red onion and red pepper salad with lots of lime juice and lime wedges for no extra *ProPoints* values.

*Preparation and cooking time 40 minutes*

350 g (12 oz) turkey mince
2 teaspoons red Thai curry paste
1 egg, beaten
2 tablespoons cornflour
zest of 2 limes
a small bunch of fresh coriander, chopped
2 spring onions, sliced finely
1 red chilli, de-seeded and sliced finely
low fat cooking spray

**TO SERVE**
lime wedges

1 Put the turkey mince, red curry paste and about half the egg in a food processor and whizz until evenly blended. Transfer to a bowl.
2 Add the cornflour, lime zest, coriander, spring onions and chilli and mix well with your fingers. Add more egg if necessary to bind the mixture.
3 Divide the mixture into 12 portions and roll each into a ball then flatten slightly to make a patty.
4 Heat a large, non stick frying pan and spray with the cooking spray. Fry the cakes in batches for about 5 minutes on each side, until golden and cooked through.

**VARIATION** Try serving these turkey cakes with a salsa, a soy dipping sauce and/or some sweet chilli sauce.

# Brussels sprouts with chestnuts

**2** ProPoints value

Serves **6** **V** *if using vegetarian crème fraîche*

| *ProPoints* values per recipe | **10** | calories per serving | **75** |

Delicious at any time of the year but the perfect seasonal accompaniment to the roast Christmas turkey; see page 165.
*Preparation and cooking time 20 minutes*

**700 g (1 lb 9 oz) Brussels sprouts, washed and trimmed**
**100 g packet vacuum sealed chestnuts**
**4 tablespoons half fat crème fraîche**
**a pinch of freshly grated nutmeg**
**salt and freshly ground black pepper**

**1** Bring a large pan of water to the boil. Make a cross in the bottom of the Brussels sprouts with a sharp knife, add to the water and cook for 10 minutes until just tender.

**2** Drain and return to the hot pan. Add the chestnuts, crème fraîche, a pinch of nutmeg and seasoning. Toss together and serve.

# Teriyaki turkey noodles

**12** ProPoints value

Serves **4** ❄

| *ProPoints* values per recipe | **49** | calories per serving | **440** |

*Preparation and cooking time 25 minutes + 15 minutes standing*

**250 g (9 oz) medium egg noodles**
**600 ml (20 fl oz) boiling chicken stock**
**3 tablespoons Teriyaki sauce**
**1 tablespoon vegetable oil**
**450 g (1 lb) turkey breasts, cut into thin strips**
**175 g (6 oz) carrots, peeled and cut into matchsticks**
**100 g (3½ oz) celery, sliced thinly**
**125 g (4½ oz) mange tout**
**a bunch of spring onions, shredded**
**2 tablespoons tomato ketchup**
**2 teaspoons cornflour**
**2 tablespoons sherry**

**1** Place the noodles in a bowl. Pour over the boiling stock. Stir in the Teriyaki sauce and leave for 15 minutes.

**2** Meanwhile, heat the oil in a large frying pan or wok and add the turkey strips. Stir fry for about 5 minutes and then add the carrots, celery and mange tout. Stir fry for a further 5 minutes.

**3** Drain the noodles, reserving the liquid, and add them to the pan or wok with the spring onions, mixing well. Add the reserved liquid and bring to the boil.

**4** Mix together the tomato ketchup, cornflour and sherry and add this to the pan. Cook, stirring, until the sauce thickens a little, and then serve straight away.

# Winter vegetable korma

Serves **4 V** ❄ *after step 2*

| *ProPoints* values per recipe | **19** | calories per serving | **240** |

Korma is one of the mildest (and creamiest) of curries. Enjoy this 'warm' dish with either 4 tablespoons of plain boiled rice, for 6 *ProPoints* values, or ½ medium naan bread, for 6 *ProPoints* values.

*Preparation time 10 minutes l Cooking time 20 minutes*

1 tablespoon vegetable oil

2 large onions, sliced

2 garlic cloves, crushed

1 tablespoon ground cumin

1 tablespoon ground coriander

1 teaspoon ground turmeric

1 teaspoon ground ginger or 4 cm (1½ inch) fresh root ginger, grated

1 tablespoon plain flour

450 ml (16 fl oz) vegetable stock

1 tablespoon tomato purée

225 g (8 oz) carrots, peeled and sliced

225 g (8 oz) parsnips, peeled and chopped

275 g (9½ oz) cauliflower florets

425 g can chick peas, rinsed and drained

110 g (4 oz) button mushrooms, halved

4 tablespoons low fat natural yogurt

salt

2 tablespoons chopped fresh coriander or parsley, to garnish

**1** Heat the oil in a large, lidded pan, add the onions and cook gently for 5 minutes, until softened and golden. Add the garlic and stir in the ground spices. Cook for a minute. Sprinkle on the flour and cook for a further minute.

**2** Blend in the vegetable stock until smooth, add the tomato purée, carrots and parsnips. Bring to the boil, cover and simmer for 10 minutes. Add the cauliflower, chick peas and mushrooms and simmer for a further 10 minutes.

**3** Season with salt, take the pan off the heat and lightly swirl in the yogurt. Serve garnished with the chopped herbs.

TOP TIP For a hotter curry, add ½–1 teaspoon chilli powder at step 1 with the other spices. For a quick alternative, replace all the vegetables with zero *ProPoints* value frozen mixed vegetables. The *ProPoints* values will be 2 per serving.

# Festive spice cookies

**U 4** *ProPoints value*

Makes **20** cookies **V**

| **ProPoints** values per recipe | **84** | calories per cookie | **175** |

These cookies are especially good for cutting into shapes for Christmas decorations or party treats.
*Preparation and cooking time 35 minutes*

low fat cooking spray
400 g (14 oz) plain flour
100 g (3½ oz) self raising flour
1 teaspoon baking powder
1 teaspoon bicarbonate of soda
1 teaspoon ground ginger
1 teaspoon ground cinnamon
¼ teaspoon nutmeg
125 g (4½ oz) low fat spread
125 g (4½ oz) soft brown sugar
3 tablespoons black treacle
2 tablespoons golden syrup

1  Preheat the oven to Gas Mark 4/180°C/fan oven 160°C and lightly coat a baking tray with the cooking spray.

2  Sift the flours, baking powder, bicarbonate of soda and spices together into a large bowl and make a well in the middle. In a saucepan melt the low fat spread, sugar, treacle and syrup then pour into the well. Add 2 tablespoons of water and mix together.

3  Turn out on to a floured surface and roll out to about ½ cm (¼ inch) thick. Cut into shapes and place on the baking tray, working quickly while the dough is still warm.

4  Bake for 10 minutes or until the cookies are slightly risen and a dark golden brown. They should still be slightly soft in the middle as they will harden on cooling. If using as decorations, make holes to hang them whilst they are still warm and soft.

5  Transfer to a wire rack to cool then decorate if you wish.

# Mincemeat surprises

**U 3** *ProPoints value*

Makes **15** **V** *if using vegetarian mincemeat*

| **ProPoints** values per recipe | **41** | calories per tart | **100** |

A lovely winter dish to serve with low fat custard (remember to add the **ProPoints** values).
*Preparation time 10 minutes l Cooking time 20 minutes*

250 g (9 oz) ready made puff pastry
150 g (5½ oz) luxury mincemeat
icing sugar, for dusting

1  Preheat the oven to Gas Mark 6/200°C/fan oven 180°C.

2  Roll half the pastry out to fit a small, non stick baking tin.

3  Spread with the mincemeat.

4  Roll out the rest of the pastry and use to top the mincemeat. Sprinkle with a little sugar.

5  Bake in the preheated oven for 20 minutes.

6  Cool in the tin for 5 minutes and then cut into 15 portions.

# Little Christmas puddings

Makes **8** puddings **V**

| ProPoints values per recipe | 49 | calories per serving | 215 |

Serve each little pudding with a spoonful of crème fraîche if you wish; just remember to add the *ProPoints* values.

*Preparation time 30 minutes + 1 day soaking l Cooking time 1 hour + 1 hour to reheat (or 30 seconds to microwave)*

**175 g (6 oz) sultanas**

**175 g (6 oz) currants**

**50 g (1¾ oz) glacé cherries, halved**

**a kettleful of boiling water**

**75 ml (3 fl oz) rum or brandy**

**½ teaspoon low fat spread**

**100 g (3½ oz) carrots, peeled and finely grated**

**75 g (2¾ oz) fresh white breadcrumbs**

**finely grated zest and juice of a small orange**

**1 teaspoon ground mixed spice**

**50 g (1¾ oz) unrefined light or dark muscovado sugar**

**1 egg, beaten**

1 Cover the sultanas, currants and cherries with boiling water. Soak for 10 minutes, then drain well. Add the rum or brandy, then cover and leave to soak for 24 hours to swell the fruit.

2 Grease eight individual pudding basins with the low fat spread. Add the remaining ingredients to the fruit mixture and stir well. Spoon into the pudding basins, level the surfaces and cover with circles of greaseproof paper. Secure pieces of foil over each basin.

3 Steam the puddings for 1 hour, topping up the steamer with extra boiling water as required. Never allow the steamer to boil dry and always use boiling water for topping up.

4 Cool the puddings when cooked and replace the pieces of foil with fresh pieces. Store in a cool, dark place. On Christmas Day, steam the puddings for 1 hour to reheat, or microwave on High for 30 seconds per pudding, allowing them to stand for 2 minutes before serving.

# Boxing Day muffins

Makes: **12** ❄ **V** *if using vegetarian mincemeat and free-range eggs*

| *ProPoints* values per recipe | **58** | calories per serving | **180** |

A great way to start the day is with these muffins – warm and freshly made – and a mug of home-brewed coffee. They will set you up for a traditional Boxing Day walk.

*Preparation time 15 minutes l Cooking time 25 minutes*

110 g (4 oz) fresh cranberries

100 g (3½ oz) mincemeat

1 small apple, peeled, cored and grated

300 g (10½ oz) plain flour

1 teaspoon baking powder

1 teaspoon mixed spice

1 teaspoon ground cinnamon

50 g (1¾ oz) light muscovado sugar

a pinch of salt

1 egg, beaten

200 ml (7 fl oz) skimmed milk

3 tablespoons vegetable oil

**1** Preheat the oven to Gas Mark 4/180°C/fan oven 160°C. Line a muffin tray with 12 paper muffin cases. Place the cranberries, mincemeat and apple in a bowl. Mix together well.

**2** Sift the flour, baking powder, spices, sugar and salt into a separate bowl. Put the egg, milk and oil in a jug and whisk together well.

**3** Make a well in the centre of the dry ingredients and pour in the egg mixture quickly, mixing together until just blended. Do not over mix.

**4** Carefully fold in the fruit mixture. Divide between the muffin cases. Bake for 20–25 minutes until well risen and golden. Transfer to a wire rack to cool slightly before serving.

TOP TIP If you over mix any muffin mixture, the muffins will become tough, so handle with care.

VARIATIONS Replace the cranberries with 1 banana, chopped. The *ProPoints* values per muffin remain the same. Replace the mincemeat with 75 g (2¾ oz) chopped ready to eat apricots. Allow 4 *ProPoints* values per muffin.

# Index